MOVIE TRIVIA QUIZ BOOK

MOVIE
TRIVIA
QUIZ
BOOK

Jam-packed with quizzes and teasers, facts and information, the Movie Trivia Quiz Book challenges you, your friends and family every time you open it! How many films did Fred Astaire and Ginger Rogers make together? Which 1981 film marked Jerry Lewis' return to the screen? What was Garbo's first Hollywood film? Which film starred Edward G. Robinson in his last screen appearance? Which two directors teamed up to make *Raiders of the Lost Ark?* Learn the answers to these and over a thousand more questions.

The Movie Trivia Quiz Book makes movie watching so much fun. Keep it by your T.V. Stump your friends. Master all the facts.

CHAPTER ONE

Supporting Players

1. She is Katharine Ross' best friend, who suddenly starts acting strange in *The Stepford Wives*.

2. She supported Redford and Newman in their efforts to swindle a big-time crook in *The Sting*.

3. As Martin Sheen's bickering parents, they battle their way through *The Subject Was Roses*.

4. As Elizabeth Taylor's mother, she is more than willing to submit her daughter for a lobotomy in exchange for money in *Suddenly, Last Summer*.

5. Joanne Woodward finds a new understanding with him after her mother dies and she learns of the stunning disapproval she's evoked in her family in *Summer Wishes, Winter Dreams*.

6. Katharine Hepburn plays an aging, lonely woman who falls in love with him on a trip to Venice in *Summertime*.

7. She plays Eleanor Roosevelt to Ralph Bellamy's Franklin in *Sunrise at Campobello*.

8. She falls in love with William Holden, unaware that he is involved with Gloria Swanson in *Sunset Boulevard*.

9. He was the off-the-cuff narrator of this spoof on the French Revolution, *Start the Revolution Without Me*.

10. She tries to take Tracy away from Hepburn in *State of the Union*.

11. Perhaps it was type-casting, but he plays a former

Mr. Universe who trains at Jeff Bridges' gym in *Stay Hungry.*

12. He plays a crook and killer that Robert Redford and Paul Newman successfully swindle in *The Sting.*

13. He trains Mark Hamill in the ways of the Jedii Knights in *Star Wars.*

14. He supplied the voice for the evil Darth Vadar in *Star Wars* and *The Empire Strikes Back.*

15. Name the two robots who served as great supporting characters in *Star Wars* and *The Empire Strikes Back?*

16. He made one of his last screen appearances as the evil commander of the Death Star in *Star Wars.*

17. She is an invalid who cannot help Dorothy McGuire when she is menanced by a killer in *Spiral Staircase.*

18. Richard Burton makes it back to safety, but she does not, in *The Spy Who Came In From The Cold.*

19. They support Nat "King" Cole in his starring role as W.C. Handy in *St. Louis Blues.*

20. He played an amiable guard in *Stalag 17.*

21. She witnesses a brutal murder but is unable to convince the police that it actually happened in *Sisters.*

22. She helps Woody Allen escape the police-state he's awakened to find in 2173 in *Sleeper.*

23. Most of the starring and supporting roles in this Truffaut film homage are children.

24. Edward G. Robinson made his last screen appearance in a supporting role in this science-fiction film.

25. She plays a twelve-year old prostitute named Iris in Martin Scorsese's *Taxi Driver*.

26. He briefly appears in *Taxi Driver* as a passenger in Robert De Niro's cab who vows to kill his own wife and her lover.

27. Sabu has his hands full with him as an evil Visier in *The Thief of Bagdad*.

28. He is appropriately evil as Cardinal Richelieu in Richard Lester's *The Three Musketeers*.

29. She has very few lines as the spaced-out, pregnant artist wife of the saloon owner in Robert Altman's *Three Women*.

30. He is perfectly evil as the villain (and James Bond's arch-enemy) in *Thunderball*.

31. She waits patiently for Vittorio Gassman to get over his fling with Ann-Margaret in *The Tiger and the Pussycat*.

32. As Humphrey Bogart's first-mate in *To Have and Have Not*, he has a problem with the bottle.

33. She is a hard-edged school girl who has a crush on Sidney Poitier in *To Sir, With Love*.

34. He portrayed Roger Daltrey's wicked Uncle Ernie in the film of the Rock-opera, *Tommy*.

35. She plays Cosmo Topper's prudish, disapproving wife in the comedy, *Topper*.

36. These three top stars make cameo appearances in

Orson Welles' thriller, *A Touch of Evil*. The film starred Charleton Heston, Janet Leigh, and Welles himself.

37. He plays a German officer who attempts to take Paris' Art treasures out of occupied France to Nazi Germany in *The Train*.

38. Greta Garbo posed as her own twin sister to test his love for her in *Two-Faced Woman*.

39. He plays a bumbling, nervous National Guard officer faced with an invading Peter Ustinov in *Viva Max!*

40. He won an Oscar as Zapata's brother in *Viva, Zapata!*

41. He is blind Audrey Hepburn's husband in the thriller *Wait Until Dark*.

42. He is Jack Lemmon's "green" first mate in the comedy *The Wackiest Ship in the Army*.

43. As Walter Matheau's nephew, he has his hands full trying to get him re-united with George Burns in *The Sunshine Boys*.

44. He won an Oscar for best supporting actor for his role in Tennessee Williams' *Sweet Bird of Youth*. Geraldine Page and Paul Newman were the stars.

45. They play John Mills and Dorothy McGuire's children in the Disney classic, *Swiss Family Robinson*.

46. She plays a vulnerable, neurotic actress who was once involved with Woody Allen in his *Stardust Memories*.

47. She plays a pathetically un-talented singer in a comedy set in a gay bathhouse, *The Ritz*.

48. He played Paris in this Hollywood version of Shakespeare's *Romeo and Juliet*. Norma Shearer and Leslie Howard played the lovers.

49. She played an old-lady neighbor in the occult horror film, *Rosemary's Baby*.

50. He won an Oscar for his role in *Sayonara*, with Marlon Brando.

51. He is first rate in the comedy *The President's Analyst*, as an agent assigned to track down James Coburn.

52. She plays Joanne Woodwards' equally repressed fellow teacher in *Rachel, Rachel*.

53. He plays Katharine Hepburn's younger brother who breaks family wishes and gets engaged in *The Rainmaker*.

54. This veteran Hollywood actor plays an inept cattle rustler in the western parody, *Rancho Deluxe*.

55. He did the Bogart inimitation in *Play It Again, Sam*.

56. He plays Tuesday Weld's homosexual friend in *Play It As It Lays*.

57. She is Fred Astaire's ex-wife in this comedy about their daughter's upcoming marriage, *The Pleasure of His Company*.

58. She played Aunt Polly to Hayley Mills' Pollyanna in the 1960 film of the same name.

59. Shelley Winters is married to him in the disaster film, *The Poseidon Adventure*.

60. Frank Sinatra is kept by her, but he won't ditch Kim Novak in *Pal Joey*.

61. He played a tough, imposing law professor in his Oscar winning role in *The Paper Chase*.

62. She was winning as a gaudy, painted hooker chasing Ryan O'Neil in *Paper Moon*.

63. They played Allison and Selena in the movie, *Peyton Place*, which starred Lana Turner.

64. Irene Dunne is Queen Victoria to his Disraeli in *The Woodlark*.

65. She is Marion, the librarian to Robert Preston's Harold Hill in *The Music Man*.

66. This 10-year-old-actor starred opposite a very disturbed Bette Davis in *The Nanny*.

67. She won an Academy Award for her performance as the bitter wife of William Holden in *Network*.

68. He suspects Ingrid Bergman of spying and begins to slowly poison her in *Notorious*.

69. He played the evil Jud in love with Shirley Jones in *Oklahoma*.

70. He played the wily Fagin to Mark Lester's orphan in *Oliver*.

71. James Bond marries her at the end of *On Her Majesty's Secret Service*.

72. He played the emotionally unstable Billy Babbitt terrorized by Nurse Ratched in *One Flew Over the Cuckoo's Nest*.

73. Alec Guinness, as a vacuum-cleaner salesman turned spy is questioned by him in *Our Man in Havana*.

74. He is a villainous Nazi who tortures Dustin Hoffman with a dentist's drill in *The Marathon Man.*

75. He menaces Hayley Mills on the island of Crete in a tale of smugglers, *The Moonspinners.*

76. David Warner is a wacko painter out to win back this woman's affections in the comedy, *Morgan.*

77. She is an extremely capable secretary who helps Jimmy Stewart with his political battles in *Mr. Smith Goes to Washington.*

78. Dustin Hoffman discovers his brother's body in the mystery/thriller, *The Marathon Man.* Who plays his brother?

79. They played Mary Astor's children in the musical *Meet Me In St. Louis.*

80. She came out of a 20-year retirement to appear as a shady lady in Walt Disney's *The Moonspinners.*

81. He virtually steals the film *Mr. Roberts,* from stars Henry Fonda and James Cagney.

82. He plays Dr. Watson to Nicol Williamson's Sherlock Holmes in *The Seven-Percent Solution.*

83. She and Peter Sellers starred in another of the Inspector Clouseau films, *A Shot in the Dark.*

84. He comes to visit staid Henry Fonda and Olivia de Haviland with uproarious results in the comedy *The Male Animal.*

85. She is Lucille Ball's best friend Vera Charles in the musical comedy, *Mame.*

86. He plays a financial advisor with vision problems

and a weight-lifting lover in the science-fiction film *The Man Who Fell to Earth*.

87. John Wayne saves lawyer Jimmy Stewart from this villain in *The Man Who Shot Liberty Valance*.

88. In Robert Altman's *The Long Good-Bye*, he plays a nasty, un-hinged hood who smashes his girlfriend's face with a coke bottle to prove a point.

89. She plays Orson Welles' on-and-off mistress in the drama *The Long, Hot Summer*.

90. He plays a smiling funeral director in the black-comedy *The Loved One*.

91. His cameo appearance as a lunatic man-of-the-cloth is a highlight of *Little Murders*.

92. He made his first screen appearance in a low-budget Roger Corman horror film about a flesh-loving plant, *Little Shop of Horrors*. He plays a masochist who loves to have his teeth pulled.

93. He is a hermit that Michael York and Jenny Auguster encounter when they flee the doomed cities of Earth in the year 2274. The film is *Logan's Run*.

94. She is a lonely woman married to a cripple in *Lonely Hearts*. The film starred Montgomery Clift as an advice columnist too caught up in his work.

95. Gene Kelly stars in this musical as the head of an American dance troup in Paris. He falls in love with his three co-dancers in *Les Girls*; can you name them?

96. He plays the English Lord who raises Freddie Bartholomew from Brooklyn to riches in *Little Lord Fauntleroy*.

97. He played a hood who has to change his evil ways

in order to be a better influence on Shirley Temple in *Little Miss Marker*.

98. He plays a young film-maker and the man Maria Schneider plans to marry before she encounters Marlon Brando in *Last Tango in Paris*.

99. This great French actress plays a Great French actress in F. Scott Fitzgerald's *The Last Tycoon*.

100. He also appears in the above film as a labor organizer in conflict with Robert De Niro's "Monroe Starr"

101. He played a perfect cad that Dana Andrews suspects may have killed *Laura*.

102. He plays the ghost of Susannah York's former lover in *Images*.

103. He plays a crusty old shark hunter in *Jaws*.

104. She plays a demented woman who shares her lover, Bruce Dern, with her daughter in *The King of Marvin Gardens*.

105. They won Academy Awards for their respective portrayals of an unhappy, neglected wife of the high-school coach, and a grizzled pool-hall owner in *The Last Picture Show*.

106. She was Barbara Streisand's protective Jewish mother in the musical, *Funny Girl*.

107. His splashy dance number in *Funny Lady* was a stand-out.

108. John Wayne, Charleton Heston, Carroll Baker, Jose Ferrer, and Shelley Winters all made guest "cameo" appearances in the 1965 Biblical tale.

109. She is a slobbish housekeeper who begins to suspect the plot Olivia de Haviland is hatching in *Hush, Hush, Sweet Charlotte*.

110. He went from the once proud Gerald O'Hara, owner of Tara to a madman living in a dream during the course of *Gone With The Wind*.

111. She is a sophisticated fence for the jewels Humphrey Bogart and Edward G. Robinson steal in *The Amazing Dr. Clitterhouse*, and a symphathetic streetwalker in *Dead End*.

112. He won Best Supporting Actor for his portrayal of a scheming, money-hungry brother-in-law opposite Lemmon in *The Fortune Cookie*.

113. She is Liv Ullman's sophisticated mother in the comedy, *Forty Carats*. This was her first screen role since her film retirement in the thirties.

114. He was Victor Lazlo, Ingrid Bergman's husband in *Casablanca*.

115. He portrays a has-been American movie star in a send-up of his own former roles in *After the Fox*.

116. One of her most memorable roles is as Bette Davis' maid in *All About Eve*.

117. He won an Academy Award as Dustin Hoffman and Robert Redford's hard-hitting editor in *All The President's Men*.

118. She played Norma Shearers' daughter in the all-female comedy, *The Women*.

119. He was memorable in his role as the High Lama in Frank Capra's *Lost Horizon*.

120. He was Dr. Zachov in the popular Flash Gordon

series.

121. She was unforgettable as the very proper Aunt "Pittypat" Hamilton in *Gone With The Wind*.

122. He was Bela Lugosi's pawn and servant, Renfield, in *Dracula*.

123. He was Gary Cooper's hobo pal, the Colonel, in *Meet John Doe*.

124. She sought revenge against Bette Davis, who had murdered her husband in *The Letter*.

125. He is John Barrymore's fast-talking agent in the all-star comedy, *Dinner at Eight*.

126. He appeared in a variety of films, from comedies to gangster movies. His few scenes as Humphrey Bogart's soon-to-be-dead partner, Miles Archer, in *The Maltese Falcon* are memorable.

127. He appeared as a jolly, hard-drinking, hard-fighting "pal" in films such as *Mr. Smith Goes to Washington*, *Mildred Pierce*, and *The Male Animal*.

128. She won an Oscar for best Supporting Actress as Alma in *From Here to Eternity*.

129. This child actor got his big chance when the producers of *The Member of the Wedding*, decided to cast him in the role opposite Julie Harris.

130. He stood out in his supporting role as a sadistic hood in *The Big Heat*.

131. He was the ultimate supporting player in his portrayal of Dr. Watson in the Sherlock Holmes series.

132. He won an Academy Award for his decadent nightclub M.C. in *Cabaret*.

133. He plays James Dean's wishy-washy father in *Rebel Without A Cause*.

134. He played a sadistic killer who torments a blind Audrey Hepburn in *Wait Until Dark*.

135. He played Bette Davis' fiance and the object of Anne Baxter's scheming in *All About Eve*.

136. Her opening number, "Think Pink" was a show stopper in 1957's *Funny Face*.

137. He was known for his nervous bluster. His roles included a fussy valet in *Top Hat* and a domineering dance school manager in *Swing Time*.

138. He sings while Bogart and Bacall look on, in the thriller *To Have and Have Not*.

139. She has the distinction of being the first black actress to win an Academy Award.

140. How many roles did Frank Morgan play in *The Wizard of Oz?*

141. He was famous for his villains and down-on-their-luck actors. One of his great comedy performances was in *Gold Diggers of 1933*.

142. His supporting role as Sylvester Stallone's crusty old trainer in *Rocky* is one of the highlights in this wonderful film.

143. Robert Donat is shocked to discover he is the villain with the missing finger in Hitchcock's *The 39 Steps*.

144. His few minutes spent dying at the beginning of this Art Carney, Lilly Tomlin comedy/adventure are memorable and provides the mystery that fuels this film.

145. His portrayal as the merciless, totally evil villain in *The Mask of Dimitrios* paved the way for his type-casting in a series of 40's films.

146. A big box office draw in her sixties musicals, she has recently garnered much critical praise for her performance in Dudley Moore's "*10*".

147. He supported Mae West (no easy task) in *She Done Him Wrong*, as the saloon boss, Gus Jordan.

148. She plays a deposed Russian countess in Garbo's first comedy, *Ninotchka*.

149. He set the style for charming, calculating cruel heavies in films such as *Destry Rides Again* and *Beau Geste*.

150. She played Dale Arden to Buster Crabbe's Flash Gordon in the films of the same name.

151. His performances as Gloria Swanson's faithful servant in *Sunset Boulevard* added to the tension in this film.

152. They played the "other couple" in *Who's Afraid of Virginia Woolf?*

153. He made his film debut in *Baby Doll* in 1956, with his screen credits including *The Misfits*, *Lord Jim*, and *MacKenna's Gold*.

154. She won Academy Awards for *The Diary of Anne Frank* and *A Patch of Blue*, and has cornered the market on tough-mouthed, big-woman parts.

155. This great character actor is best remembered as the busy bank examiner J. Pinkerton Snoopington in the W.C. Fields classic, *The Bank Dick*.

156. This excellent supporting actor is best

remembered as the father of the Morgan clan in *How Green Was My Valley*.

157. As Sugar Boy, he embodied the role of the neurotic, tough hood in *All The King's Men*.

158. His line, "round up the usual suspects" brought a look of relief to Bogart's face at the end of *Casablanca*.

159. He won an Oscar for his performance as Paul Gauguin in *Lust for Life*.

160. He is best remembered for his portrayal of Kris Kringle in the classic *Miracle on 34th Street*.

161. She stood out as Isabelle Steers in the all-star cast of *The Misfits*.

162. He is perfectly in character in his role as Colonel Pickering in *My Fair Lady*.

163. As a supporting player, he was a better revolutionary! However, in his youth, this future leader was a player in the Xavier Cugat film *Holiday in Mexico*, in 1946.

164. He was always type-cast in westerns as an Indian Chief, appearing in films such as *Stagecoach* and *She Wore a Yellow Ribbon*. Incidentally, he was also the model for the Indian Head nickel.

165. He was immortalized in his supporting role in *Grand Hotel*, when he said, "Always the same. People come. People go. Nothing ever happens."

166. In *Ruggles of Red Gap*, Charles Laughton plants a kiss on this classic supporting actress' face.

167. He was Carolyn Keene's sidekick in the Nancy Drew adventure series films.

168. She is best remembered for her classic line, "I don't know nothin' 'bout birthin' babies!" from *Gone With The Wind.*

169. He played Baby Dumpling (Alexander) in the *Blondie* series in the 40's.

170. This great supporting actor co-starred with Bette Davis in the 1941 film, *The Man Who Came To Dinner.*

171. She turned in one of her stellar performances in *Witness for the Prosecution,* as Charles Laughton's nagging nurse. (HINT: She was Laugthon's real-life wife.)

172. He gives a strong supporting performance as Jimmy Stewart's boozing assistant in *The Court-Martial of Billy Mitchell.*

173. He has appeared in character roles that range from *The Lady from Shanghai* to *Somebody Up There Likes Me.* He is probably best remembered for his role as Bernstein in *Citizen Kane.*

174. He played Claudette Colbert's irate daddy in *It Happened One Night* and father-figures in a slew of thirties films.

175. In the forties, this supporting player was all over in films such as *The Strawberry Blonde, Gentleman Jim,* and *They Drive By Night.*

176. He turned fussiness into an art-form in films such as *Top Hat* with Fred Astaire.

177. He played an unending series of bartenders, drunks and doctors in films of the 40's and 50's.

178. This villain specialized in playing spies, madmen, and Nazis in the 30's and 40's. But he is probably remembered best as the German Colonel Humphrey

Bogart kills in *Casablanca*.

179. This actress specialized in crusty, busy-body biddies, such as Aunt Miranda in *Rebecca of Sunnybrook Farm*.

180. She won an Academy Award for her portrayal of Mrs. O'Leery, whose cow started the Chicago fire. She also had success in *Gold Diggers of 1935* and *My Man Godfrey*.

181. Preston Sturgess was fond of using this actress in films such as *Hail The Conquering Hero*. Her finest performance may be as the iron-willed old woman in *Intruder in the Dust*.

182. He was typecast in kind, sympathetic roles in films such as *This is the Army*, and *The Moon's Our Home*.

183. She was memorable as Lady Marion's hand-maiden in *Robin Hood*.

184. He is particularly memorable as Roslynn Russell's shiftless landlord in *My Sister Eileen*.

185. He played the object of Bette Davis' affections in *Whatever Happened to Baby Jane?*

186. His bullfrog voice made him unforgettable in films that ranged from *Topper* to *Robin Hood*.

187. He showed up as Irish Cops, the hard-drinking best-friend, and a host of nervous reporters in the 30's and 40's.

188. She played the intended wife of the monster in the 1935 film *The Bride of Frankenstein*.

189. She was unforgettable as the snobbish and quite mad Mrs. Van Hopper in *Rebecca*.

190. Also in *Rebecca*, this one-time leading man turned in another of his sterling performances as a cad.

191. Although he was only on the screen for a very short time in *Casablanca* his entreaty to Rick to save him is unforgettable.

192. As a supporting actress, she was a better heiress. She appeared in only one sound film, the W.C. Fields, George Burns and Gracie Allen wacky comedy, *International House*.

193. He played blustery English Gentlemen in such films as *Bombshell* and *Three Feathers*.

194. She always played Andy Hardy's sister.

195. He was the piano player, Sam, in *Casablanca*.

196. She is probably best known for her character, Mrs. Olson, in the Folger's Coffee TV ad campaign. However, she was a supporting actress in hundreds of B-movies and first-line releases.

197. Although he began his career as a Shakesperean actor, and has appeared in supporting roles in films such as *Drums Along the Mohawk, Stagecoach,* and *The Grapes of Wrath*, he is probably best remembered for his roles in Grade-B Horror Flicks.

198. This fine supporting actress made over 70 films, but is probably best remembered for the role of Trina in *I Remember Mama*. Can you name her?

199. How many films has John Carradine made?

200. She has appeared in over 80 films, that range from *Witness For the Prosecution,* and *Stormy Weather* to *Doctor Doolittle*. I'm sure you'd know the face, but do you know this great supporting actress' name?

201. She is (perhaps) everyone's favorite supporting actress! She has held down second bill to Bette Davis in *June Bride*, Doris Day in *I'll See You In My Dreams* and Rosalind Russell in *The Trouble With Angels*.

202. He once claimed to be Hollywood's unhappiest actor in the forties, because he was always "cast as a blood-letting...evil old man." Among his films were *The Monster and the Girl, Arise, My Love,* and *Dr. Renaults' Secret.* However, he is probably best remembered as the evil genius of crime, Moriarty, in the Sherlock Holmes adventures.

203. He usually played the great screen neurotics, personified by his great performance as *Wilbur,* the Fat Man's psychotic assistant in *The Maltese Falcon.*

204. In the 40's his cantankerous personality and grizzled appearance made him the perfect foil for Roy Rogers and Dale Evans in their Westerns.

CHAPTER TWO

Leading Ladies

1. She falls in love with Warren Beatty in *Splendor in the Grass*.

2. As Pookie Adams, she was nominated for an Academy Award for *The Sterile Cuckoo*.

3. She plays a steely librarian who refuses to take a controversial book from the shelves simply to appease local politicians in *Storm Center*.

4. Her taunting, teasing, flirting eventually leads to her rape in Sam Peckinpah's *Straw Dogs*.

5. She plays Siamese twins in Brian De Palma's homage to Hitchcock, *Sisters*. She also hangs around with the Man-of-Steel in *Superman*.

6. She plays the den mother to a bunch of young, beauty-contest entrants in the comedy, *Smile*.

7. She takes the side of the Indians in *Soldier Blue*.

8. She is a poor sharecropper's wife in the 30's, who must cope with her families' work load when her husband is sent to prison in *Sounder*.

9. She was the hooker with the heart of gold in the 1969 musical, *Sweet Charity*.

10. She plays a psychiatrist who becomes involved with George C. Scott because he thinks he's Sherlock Holmes. The film is *They Might Be Giants*.

11. She wants revenge on Tyrone Power because of his nasty newspaper articles on her in the comedy *That Wonderful Urge*.

12. They exchange personalities in Robert Altman's tale of blended lives and the frail nature of personality, *Three Women*.

13. She plays an emotionally unstable woman, drawn into an affair with George C. Scott in *Petulia*.

14. She plays Fred Astaire's daughter in *The Pleasure of His Company*. Unfortunately, her husband-to-be, Tab Hunter, seems boring when she compares him to Astaire.

15. She co-starred with a haughty Laurence Olivier in the love story, *The Prince and the Showgirl*.

16. She portrays a zany, imposteur-princess on a trip aboard a luxury ocean-liner in *The Princess Comes Across*.

17. She starred in husband John Cassavetes' movie portrait of a woman who suffers because she is "different" in *A Woman Under the Influence*.

18. She becomes pregnant, but she isn't sure who the father is in the comedy *Miracle at Morgan's Creek*.

19. She almost destroys Jose Ferrer with a love that turns to jealousy in *The Shrike*.

20. She portrays the governess who becomes ensnared in the seeming possession of two young children, *The Innocents*, based on Henry James' "The Turn of the Screw"

21. She plays an invalid who searches for happiness with Van Heflin in *Invitation*.

22. She plays the title role in this comedy of a prostitute and a man who falls in love with her in *Irma La Douce*.

23. She is an unemployed model who rents a billboard on Times Square and becomes famous overnight in *It Should Happen to You*.

24. Her films included *Fast and Loose*, *Becky Sharp*, and *Woman Chases Man*.

25. She starred opposite Ronald Coleman in the costume-classic *The Prisoner of Zenda*.

26. She stars as Fanny Brice in the delightful musical *Funny Girl*. Omar Shariff is her romantic interest.

27. She stars as a woman slipping into schizophrenia in the Robert Altman movie, *Images*.

28. She starred in her first film in 1931, *The Sin of Madelon Claudet*.

29. Her 30's musicals included *She Learned About Sailors*, *Every Night At Eight*, and *Wake Up and Live*.

30. She starred in one of the first important "women's" picture of the 70's, *An Unmarried Woman*.

31. Her performance as Sylvester Stallone's horribly shy girlfriend in *Rocky* is one of the delights of the film.

32. Originally, she had wanted Montgomery Clift to co-star with her as a troubled, homosexual army officer. Eventually the role in *Reflections In A Golden Eye* fell to Marlon Brando.

33. She was America's tap-dancing sweetheart, and she rescues the show in Busby Berkley's *42nd Street*.

34. A child star in her own right, she played Shirley Temple's selfish friend in *Bright Eyes*.

35. She played Judy Garland's mother in two films, *Listen, Darling* and *Meet Me In St. Louis*. She was a major star of the 30's and 40's.

36. She played Judy Garland's mother in *Broadway Melody of 1938*, to the hilt.

37. She danced her way into the hearts of millions in musicals like *Honolulu* and *Broadway Melody of 1938*.

38. Although she starred in many Hollywood films, she is best remembered for G.W. Papsts' *Pandora's Box*, and *The Diary of a Lost Girl*.

39. She played Beauty to Jean Marais' Beast in Jean Cocteau's *Beauty and the Beast*.

40. William Baschart and Anthony Quinn are her unlikely co-stars in Fellini's early masterpiece, *La Strada*.

41. They starred as Helen Keller and Annie Sullivan in *The Miracle Worker*.

42. She starred with Montgomery Clift in the story of the Tennessee Valley Authority's Dam program, *Wild River*.

43. One of the premier sex symbols of the sixties, she co-starred with Sean Connery in the first James Bond feature, *Dr. No*.

44. She played Katharine to Robert Donat's Mr. Chips in the 1937 Award winner, *Goodbye, Mr. Chips*.

45. Death, in the form of Fredric March falls in love with her in *Death Takes A Holiday*.

46. Her reply to Humphrey Bogart's query "how

could anybody like a face like this?" in *In A Lonely Place* is a movie classic.

47. She co-starred with Bogart in *The Barefoot Contessa*.

48. She was Cary Grant's wife in the uproarious comedy *I Was A Male War Bride*.

49. She proves to be more than a match for Big Business in *The Solid Gold Cadillac*.

50. She played a cold-hearted woman out to make Spencer Tracy, politically, in *State of the Union*.

51. She played a young star unable to cope with the pressures of stardom in *Valley of the Dolls*.

52. She was the first actress to demand and receive one million dollars for starring in a film. The film she first asked it for was a major Hollywood epic co-starring Rex Harrison and Richard Burton. Can you name the woman and the film?

53. This operatic young singer got her first screen kiss from a very young Robert Stack in the 1939 film *First Love*.

54. Many critics felt she vindicated herself in this, her sixth (and first non-singing) role as a young, New York housewife trying to secure her rights.

55. In this 1970 horror film, this great actress of the 30's and 40's investigates the missing link. This film is *Trog*.

56. Herbert Marshall and Melvyn Douglas vie for her affections in this 1937 film.

57. She plays a woman with sleep-walking problems in the 1951 film, *Half Angel*.

58. In *Bedazzled*, she makes a cameo appearance as Lust.

59. In this Luis Bunuel classic, she plays a frigid housewife who spends her afternoons as a prostitute.

60. In *Damn Yankees*, she played the devil's dancing man-eater, Lola.

61. *Up the Down Staircase* starred her as a young teacher in a very tough school.

62. Her films include *Blithe Spirit*, *The V.I.P.'s* and *Murder Ahoy*.

63. She sings, dances and flaunts her "divine decadence" as Sally Bowles in the musical *Cabaret*.

64. Although she is primarily thought of in light-weight, sugary parts, Hitchcock cast her opposite James Stewart in the '56 remake of *The Man Who Knew Too Much*.

65. She played the sultry lady of the title, in *Lady from Shanghai*.

66. Name three films Lauren Bacall starred in with Humphrey Bogart.

67. These two sex-symbols co-starred together in *Gentlemen Prefer Blondes*.

68. She made her screen reputation in gangster movies like *The Big Heat* and *In A Lonely Place*.

69. Although she is primarily remembered for her tough-lady screen roles, this actress was also a premier Hollywood director.

70. Alan Ladd played her romantic interest in *The Blue Dalia*, but she is best remembered for the way she

wore her hair.

71. She helped Gregory Peck discover his real identity in the Hitchcock thriller, *Spellbound*.

72. She starred in the first full-length Disney musical to feature real people and not just animated characters.

73. Name two Audrey Hepburn musicals in which she starts out as a "plain jane" and winds up a beauty.

74. She played Mrs. Cole Porter to Cary Grants' Mr. in *Night and Day*.

75. *Paint Your Wagon* was the only musical in her short career. The musical also featured the dubious singing talents of Clint Eastwood and Lee Marvin.

76. Who played the title role in *Sweet Charity*?

77. Her film credits include *On the Avenue*, and *Alexander's Ragtime Band*.

78. Who starred in and claims the title song as her "legacy" in *Stormy Weather*.

79. Although she's best known for her powerhouse singing, she starred in movies such as *Anything Goes*, *Call Me Madam*, and *There's No Business Like Show Business*.

80. She pioneered the "aqua" musical for MGM. Can you name her?

81. Name the films Elizabeth Taylor made with Montgomery Clift.

82. Grace Kelly made two films with Bing Crosby. Name them.

83. Name two famous screen Cleopatra's other than Elizabeth Taylor.

84. Richard Burton played her romantic interest in the Biblical epic *The Robe*.

85. Who played Ma Kettle in the famous series of Ma and Pa Kettle movies?

86. She is best remembered as the beautiful mistress in *Room at the Top*.

87. Who was the female lead in the Bob Hope/Bing Crosby "road" pictures?

88. She played the second wife to Lawrence Olivier in *Rebecca*.

89. Joan Crawford and Bette Davis starred together in *Whatever Happened to Baby Jane*, but who co-starred with Ms. Davis in *Hush...Hush, Sweet Charlotte?*

90. Although she is a great dramatic actress, she has made many wonderful comedies such as *Adam's Rib*, *Pat and Mike*, and *Desk Set*.

91. Clark Gable played opposite her in *It Happened One Night*.

92. What was Claudette Colbert's famous retort to Jean Harlow's mis-pronounciation of her name?

93. Who replaced Carol Channing in the film version of *Hello Dolly?*

94. Her real name was Frances Gumm.

95. Who played the title role opposite Fred Astaire in *Funny Face?*

96. How many times has Elizabeth Taylor been on the cover of *Life* magazine?

97. Who was the youngest actress ever to appear on the cover of *Time* magazine?

98. What was Elizabeth Taylor's first film?

99. What movie boasted a cast of 135 women and not one appearance by a male actor?

100. Name 3 famous actresses who began their career as models.

101. What famous actress was the first centerfold for *Playboy* magazine?

102. How many movies did Katharine Hepburn appear in with Spencer Tracy?

103. Who is the youngest person to ever win an Oscar?

104. In Hollywood's quest for novelty, this ice-skating star was second only to Esther Williams.

105. She consistently played Groucho's straight woman in Marx Brothers films such as *A Night at the Opera* and *Animal Crackers*.

106. What was Mary Pickford's final film?

107. She finds out that Jane Wyatt and Donald Cook are not her real parents in *Our Very Own*.

108. She manages to pass for white, but moving back to the South causes problems for her in *Pinky*.

109. They are sisters in the Alfred Hitchcock thriller *Psycho*.

110. She plays Delilah to Victor Mature's Samson in the Biblical drama *Samson & Delilah*.

111. John Wayne and Jeffrey Hunter discover she is being raised by Indians in the cult-western *The Searchers*.

112. They light up the screen in the WW II comedy *A Foreign Affair*.

113. She plays a loose woman in the 17th Century drama with George Sanders and Cornell Wilde.

114. Anthony Perkins played her son, Gary Cooper her husband in this story of peaceful Quakers caught in the Civil War. The film was *Friendly Persuasion*.

115. She played a scheming Englishwoman who allies herself with a swashbuckling French pirate in the costume spectacular *Frenchman's Creek*.

CHAPTER THREE

The Male Lead

1. He plays a paralyzed war veteran who learns to adjust, in *The Men*.

2. He played a small-time nightclub comic who becomes involved with big-time hoods in *Mickey One*.

3. He is a fortune-hunter who chooses Marlene Dietrich over money in this film.

4. He has the title roll as a gambler down on his luck who organizes a war drive bazaar to raise money for a game in *Mr. Lucky*.

5. He was cast as the greatest lover in the 18th Century in Fellini's *Casanova*.

6. He plays the founder of psychoanalysis in John Huston's *Freud*.

7. He is a world-weary stud looking for a place to settle down in the Tennessee Williams drama, *The Fugitive Kind*.

8. They g nered loads of critical attention as two small-time hoods on the run in the French film, *Going Places*.

9. He is anxious to become a WW I flying ace in *The Blue Max*.

10. Jean Simmons and he are ship-wrecked on a beautiful desert island where they fall in love in the 1948 version of *The Blue Lagoon*.

11. He plays a psychotic terrorist out to destroy the

Superbowl and the attending U.S. President in *Black Sunday*.

12. He plays an animal-loving cowpoke angered by brutal endurance horse races in *Bite the Bullet*.

13. They starred as the ultimate buddies in a story of friendship and drifting, *Scarecrow*.

14. Liv Ullmann is his wife in the searing examination of a decaying marriage, *Scenes From A Marriage*.

15. Kim Stanley manipulates him into a kidnap plot in *Seance on a Wet Afternoon*.

16. He finds an orphan in the rubble of post-war Europe in the tearjerker, *The Searcher*.

17. An entire town suspects him of murdering his wife in *The Second Woman*.

18. He begins the film as an old man who discovers an organization that can make him young again in *Seconds*.

19. He discovers he must fight to end sabotage in a California shipyard. The film is *Secret Command*.

20. He and Margaret O'Brien discover a magical, secluded garden in 1949's *The Secret Garden*.

21. Deborah Kerr, as a spinster, falls in love with him in *Separate Tables*.

22. They played the *Sergeants' Three* of the title in this film.

23. As James Fox's butler, he completely insinuates himself into his employer's life in *The Servant*.

24. He becomes John Brown, the abolitionist in the

Civil War drama, *Seven Angry Men*.

25. They play father and son in this drama of a washed-up rodeo star and his hard-drinking father, *Junior Bonner*.

26. Irene Dunne is the career-minded stage star he romances in *Joy of Living*.

27. Two brothers plot to steal the Crown Jewels and then succeed at doing it. The comedy is *The Jokers*.

28. *Johnny Angel* starred him as a merchant marine who unravels several mysteries including the death of his father.

29. He is riveting in his role as a racist, bigoted hate-monger in *Joe*.

30. He played the title role in the musical *Jesus Christ, Superstar*.

31. He has the title role of a young Jewish cellist who falls in love with the Gentile dancer in *Jeremy*.

32. Will Geer teaches him what he needs to know to become a mountain man in *Jeremiah Johnson*.

33. He plays a choreographer remarkably like the director, Bob Fosse, in *All That Jazz*.

34. He co-stars with Lisa Minelli as her bisexual lover in *Cabaret*.

35. Goldie Hawn falls for him in his role, as a blind, totally self-sufficient man in *Butterflies Are Free*.

36. He is a vicious, hard-drinking University professor forced to deal with the break-up of his marriage and the leaving of his gay lover in *Butley*.

37. They play frustrated cops stuck on the junkie-and-hooker arrest circuit in *Busting*.

38. Joan Goodfellow is the school tramp who finally falls in love with him in *Buster and Billie*.

39. A comedy about a gangster who takes refuge in a monastery, it is a change-of-pace from his regular films. The movie is *Brother Orchid*.

40. Lillian Gish fell in love with him as a Chinese man in the silent tragedy, *Broken Blossoms*.

41. He is forced to order his men to build *The Bridge on the River Kwai*.

42. Although he hates kids, he is forced to convince one to pose as his son. The result is the comedy *The Bride Goes Wild*.

43. He believes that he can fly in Robert Altman's spaced-out comedy, *Brewster McCloud and His Flying Machine*.

44. Audrey Hepburn is the New York playgirl he becomes involved with in the musical *Breakfast at Tiffany's*.

45. Primarily known as a director, he is cast opposite Gina Lollobrigida in this high-spirited comedy, *Bread, Love and Dreams*.

46. *Bound for Glory*, cast him as the legendary folksinger, Woody Guthrie.

47. They played the male leads in this late 60's comedy of sexual mores, *Bob and Carol and Ted and Alice*.

48. In *Blume in Love*, he is divorced from but still passionately in love with ex-wife Susan Anspach.

49. This remake of Valentino's *Blood and Sand* casts him in the role of the matador.

50. He made his debut in 1929 as *Disraeli* and moved into the talkies in films such as *Cardinal Richelieu.* He specialized in historical characters, among them, Voltaire and Alexander Hamilton.

51. He starred opposite Greta Garbo as the man who made her laugh in *Ninotchka*.

52. Disney cast him as an Indian boy who falls in love with a white girl in *The Light in the Forest*.

53. He starred as Henry Aldrich in the 1941 comedy *Life With Henry*.

54. He is saved from alcoholism by his daughter, Ida Lupino, in *Life Begins at Eight-Thirty*.

55. He is the son of a murdered Viking chieftain fighting to regain his title in *Last of the Vikings*.

56. A plague has wiped out most of the Earth's population, and turned the rest to zombies. He is the only remaining man in *The Last Man On Earth*.

57. He invites a number of "friends" on a Riviera cruise to discover which one murdered his wife. The film is *The Last Of Shiela*.

58. He buys a tenement in Brooklyn with the idea of converting it to a private home. However, he hasn't reckoned on the black tenants in *The Landlord*.

59. If you can imagine, Brigitte Bardot goes to great lengths to make him pay attention to her in *La Parisienne*.

60. They come out at odds as prisoners-of-war in *King Rat*.

61. He plays a Scottish private near the end of WW I. Sent to investigate a German bomb, he finds only the charming inhabitants of the local asylum. The film is *King of Hearts.*

62. A deposed European King comes to New York in the heyday of McCarthyism in *A King in New York.* Who played the King in this film, banned in America for over 10 years?

63. He falls in love with Lilly Tomlin, in spite of age and background in *Moment by Moment.*

64. They come up at odds in the epic about the battle of *Kartoum.*

65. He stars as Jessie James in this tale of Quantrill's Raiders in *Kansas Raiders.*

66. Australia is the background for this mistaken-identity mystery. He stars as the sailor drawn into the plot in *Kangaroo.*

67. For his performance as Sir Thomas More in *A Man For All Seasons,* this actor won an Academy Award.

68. He made his screen reputation as *Billy Budd,* and in films such as *Far From The Maddening Crowd* and *A Season in Hell.*

69. He won an Oscar for his portrayal of a vicious, police chief in *In The Heat of the Night.*

70. His performance as a would-be hustler in *Midnight Cowboy* made him a star.

71. He made his film debut in Hitchcock's *The Lady Vanishes.* Other films include *The Loneliness of the Long Distance Runner, The Hill,* and *David Cooperfield.*

72. This fine actor was knighted in 1947. His films include *Thing to Come*, *Richard III*, *The Heiress*, and *The Looking-Glass War*.

73. This great black singer and actor made a number of films. Some of them are *The Emperor Jones*, *Showboat*, and *Tales of Manhattan*.

74. He is seen primarily in villain roles. He won an Academy Award for his performance in *Judgment at Nuremberg*. Other films of his are *The Young Lions*, *The Man in the Glass Booth*, and *The Deadly Affair*.

75. He comes back to the screen in John Waters *Polyester*, with Divine as his co-star.

76. Diana Ross is his co-star in this account of Billie Holiday's life, *Lady Sings the Blues*.

77. Jean Arthur falls in love with him but he has no intention of being tied down in *A Lady Takes A Chance*.

78. These two fine British comics team up in this story of an elaborate bank heist foiled by an old woman, *The Ladykillers*.

79. He specialized in villains in such films as *Shane*, *Barrabas*, and *the Big Knife*.

80. A beautiful woman is accused of murdering her husband in *The Paradine Case*. He plays the young lawyer who falls in love with her while defending her.

81. His screen roles invariably are of strong personalities. Some of his screen credits are *Eyewitness*, *Royal Hunt of the Sun*, and *The Sound of Music*.

82. *A Raisin in the Sun*, *Porgy and Bess*, *Lilies of the*

Field, To Sir With Love and *Guess Who's Coming To Dinner* are just a few of his film credits.

83. His non-acting style made him a star. His films include *Bullitt, The Reivers,* and *The Great Escape.*

84. He won an Academy Award for best supporting actor in *A Streetcar Named Desire.* Lately, he is seen as a spokesman for American Express.

85. He has become one of America's top box-office draws. His films include *Hopscotch, The Sunshine Boys, The Fortune Cookie,* and *Cactus Flower.*

86. This great French singer has also had a long and varied film career. Some of his movies are *Z, The Wages of Fear,* and *On A Clear Day You Can See Forever.*

87. His screen appearance as a down-on-his-luck, small time hood in Louis Malle's *Atlantic City* has gathered critical praise.

88. They were perhaps the screen's finest comedy duo in such silent classics as *The Battle of the Century, Wrong Again.* and *Big Business.*

89. His Mr. Moto movies in the late 30's were extremely popular.

90. He was type-cast as a heroic, likeable guy throughout his film career. His films include *Union Pacific, Wells Fargo* and *The Virginian.*

91. He usually appears as suave villains or lady-killers. This German actor's films include *I Aim at the Stars, Inn of the Sixth Happiness,* and *The Longest Day.*

92. Many consider his prime characterization to have been *Frankenstein.* This famous screen actor also

appeared in *The Body Snatchers* and *Isle of the Dead*.

93. He played a skinny comedic counterpoint to Fatty Arbuckle in over 14 films such as *The Butcher Boy*. A star of slapstick comedy on his own, some of his films were *Sherlock Junior*, *The Cameraman*, and *College*. His last screen appearance was in *A Funny Thing Happened on the Way to the Forum*.

94. This actor's name is virtually synonymous with film epics. They include *The Agony and the Ecstasy*, *The Greatest Story Ever Told* and *El Cid*.

95. With Peter Fonda, he changed the minds of Hollywood's establishment with the low budget/big profit *Easy Rider*. His next feature was the excessive *The Last Movie*.

96. His rugged good looks made him the ideal star of the early 60's. Some of his films were *Pillow Talk*, *Man's Favorite Sport*, and *Send Me No Flowers*.

97. He has made a reputation in such films as *Rashomon* as Japan's top tough guy and premier actor.

98. He built his reputation as a suave and urbane ladies' man, but he and Richard Burton played long-time gay lovers in *Staircase*.

99. Simone Signoret was his mistress in the melodrama *Room at the Top*.

100. He made his reputation in silent films like *The Typhoon*. This Japanese actor also appeared in sound films such as *Bridge on the River Kwai* and *Swiss Family Robinson*.

101. He was known for his serious portrayals of regular men. His films include *They Came to Cordura*, *Stagecoach*, (the 1966 re-make) and *Shane*.

102. Mae West helped shape his off-the-cuff charm in *She Done Him Wrong*. *Charade*, *North by Northwest*, and *The Philadelphia Story* were a few of his films.

103. He played eight different roles in the black-comedy *Kind Hearts and Coronets*.

104. *The Apprenticeship of Duddy Kravitz*, *The Good-bye Girl*, and *Jaws* are a few of his films.

105. A major star of the sixties, his films include *A Man Called Horse*, *The Red Desert*, *The Guns of Navarone* and *Cromwell*.

106. He danced through Vincent Minelli's *An American in Paris*.

107. He co-starred with Gene Kelly in the musical classic *Singing in the Rain*.

108. Nicholas Roeg cast him as a reclusive rock star in *Performance*.

109. He starred in *Grand Hotel*, *Romeo and Juliet* and *Dinner at Eight*. His nickname comes from the title of his 1940 film, *The Great Profile*.

110. He plays a poor farmer in love with wealthy Julie Christie in *The Go-Between*.

111. He is Shirley MacLaine's brother. His films include *Splendor in the Grass*, *Lilith*, and *Bonnie and Clyde*.

112. His first film (silent) cast him as a female impersonator. He became known for the rough and nasty character he portrayed in *Barnacle Bill*, *Min and Bill* and *The Champ*.

113. This French leading man became a film tough-guy modeled on Bogart in films such as *Cartouche*,

That Man From Rio and *Borsalino.*

114. He played the mad dog killer Duke Mantee in *The Petrified Forest.*

115. He was a wide-mouthed comedian famous for his tearful looks. His films include *Crooks Can't Win, Pin-Up Girl, Showboat,* and *Some Like It Hot.*

116. His bald head is his trade mark. His films include *The Ten Commandments, The Magnificent Seven* and *Solomon and Sheba.*

117. His films with Elizabeth Taylor include *The Taming of the Shrew, Boom, The Sandpiper,* and *Cleopatra.*

118. He made his mark in the late sixties with *Alfie.* Other films include *The Ipcress File, The Man Who Would Be King* and *Zulu.*

119. In his own right, he is a successful film maker. His acting roles include *The Fury, Rosemary's Baby,* and *The Dirty Dozen.*

120. His cameo role as a Nazi-mutilated Jew in *Judgment at Nuremberg* was devastating.

121. His English accent and gentlemen's good looks landed him in films such as *A Tale of Two Cities, Talk of the Town,* and *Beau Geste.*

122. Although he is primarily known for his portrayals of James Bond, his other films include *The Anderson Tapes, Zardoz,* and *Outland.*

123. This child-actor's films include *The Kid, Old Clothes, Oliver Twist* and *The Bugle Call.*

124. His tight-lipped heroes almost never varied from film to film. His movies include *Sergeant York, The*

Virginian, and *The Fountainhead.*

125. This knighted British writer/composer starred in *The Scoundrel, Our Man in Havana* and *Boom.*

126. Judy Holiday put this crude, business tycoon character in his place in *Born Yesterday.*

127. Visconti cast him as the twisted son of a steel-producing family during the Nazi rise to power. The film was *The Damned.*

128. *Seven Days in May, Gunfight at the OK Corral, The Fury,* and *Spartacus* are just a few of this popular actor's films.

129. He became a star after the release of a low-budget spaghetti western, *A Fistfull of Dollars.*

130. His vast physical presence and handsome face lit up the silent screen in *The Mark of Zorro, The Black Pirate,* and *The Gaucho.*

131. His last film was *Network,* in which he starred as a mentally disturbed newscaster.

132. His long film career has included *War and Peace, Fail Safe, Mr. Roberts,* and *The Cheyenne Social Club.*

133. The screen chemistry between him and Rita Hayworth in *Gilda* lit up the screen in 1946.

134. His first screen role was in *The Painted Desert* in 1931, his last in *The Misfits* in 1960.

135. He has been called the premier Post-Depression tough guy for his minimal aggressive heroes. His films included *Destination Tokyo, The Postman Always Rings Tiwce,* and *Force of Evil.*

136. He reached the peak of his popularity in the 20's

as Garbo's leading man. His films include *The Merry Widow*, *La Boheme*, and *Queen Christina*.

137. His depiction of anxiety-ridden non-heroes made him a major star in the 70's. His film credits include *The Long Good-Bye*, *Getting Straight*, and *I Love My Wife*.

138. Who stood on a box for many of his love scenes in order to be taller than his leading lady?

139. What was James Dean's last film?

140. This muddled horror movie, *Curse of the Crimson Altar*, was his last screen appearance.

141. He played a self-righteous policeman in *Detective Story*.

142. Their late-sixties film, *Easy Rider*, turned them both into stars.

143. He starred in films such as *Blessed Event* and *Blonde Bombshell* and was primarily known for his ability to talk fast and deliver snappy lines.

144. Name the four famous members of the Bowery Boys, who had previously been Dead End Kids.

145. Who is the oldest actor to win an Oscar?

146. Who was the first choice for Marlon Brando's role in *On The Waterfront*?

147. What actor holds the record for Oscar nominations with no wins?

148. He played strong supporting roles in westerns such as *Drums Along the Mohawk* and *Hondo*, but came to fame on TV's *Wagon Train* series.

149. Name the first male actor to grace the cover of McCall's Magazine in over 100 years.

150. What movie did Clifton Webb make his acting debut in?

151. Can you name the actor best remembered for his portrayal of the Wolf Man?

152. These two actors are also considered art experts.

153. He won an Academy Award for his performance as Maggio in *From Here to Eternity*.

154. He first came to public attention as the child molester in Fritz Lang's classic "*M*"

155. He played the villain in the 1919 horror film *The Cabinet of Dr. Caligari*.

156. Although he is primarily remembered for his tough-guy roles, one of his most loved films is the musical *Yankee Doodle Dandy*.

157. He starred in a variety of tough-guy films including *Call Northside 777* and *Tony Rome*.

158. Who starred in the 1951 Hitchcock suspense film *Strangers on a Train*?

159. Before he ventured into TV, this man starred in musicals such as *Born to Dance* and *Red Garters*.

160. He gave life to the straw hat, the song, "*Louise*" and musicals such as *Gigi*, and *Folies Bergere*.

161. His films include *The Inspector General* and *White Christmas*.

162. Who played Stanley to Cedric Hardwicke's Livingston in the 1939 film of the famous encounter?

163. Who starred in the film version of *Prince Valiant*?

164. Name the co-stars in the classic, *Citizen Kane*.

165. Who was *The Man in the Grey Flannel Suit*?

166. He counted among his leading ladies Elizabeth Taylor, Olivia De Haviland, Katharine Hepburn, Shelley Winters and Marilyn Monroe. Who was he?

167. Name the movie Clift was filming at the time of his famous car accident.

168. He played the kept-boy of an aging ex-star in a Billy Wilder movie. Who was he?

169. Who was the mule's sidekick in six of the seven Francis the Talking Mule movies?

170. Among his movies are *Patton*, *The Hospital*, and *Rage*.

Four-Legged Screen Stars

1. Butch Jenkins talks to these animals and they talk back to him in this film.

2. A little girl who is abandoned by her parents and abused by her governess becomes highly attached to a stray dog in this film.

3. Tommy Kirk and Kevin Corcoran fall in love with an old mongrel in this Disney film.

4. Lassie outsmarts the villain in this film of our canine heroine's adventures. It stars Paul Kelly and Gary Gray.

5. One of the heroes of this film is a winged, white stallion named Pegasus.

6. Ronny Howard cannot become used to his new stepfather, Earl Holleman, and instead adopts this stray creature.

7. Fred MacMurray holds a deep and abiding love for his horse in this film.

8. A little girl befriends and saves a stallion being hunted down by ranchers who think him dangerous.

9. Barry Fitzgerald plays the trainer in this film about one of the most famous race-horses of all time.

10. A horse and boy shipwrecked on a desert island and their love for each other won critical acclaim.

11. A young Polynesian boy befriends and raises a

baby shark in this film.

12. Can you name Tom Mix's horse?

13. Eddie Arnold discovers his children can turn into bears in this fantasy-comedy.

14. Jay North and Sajid Kahn must deliver a sacred, white elephant to an Indian Temple.

15. He was a giant ape that Terry Moore and Ben Johnson try to help escape the city he is put on display in.

16. David Ladd and Pam Smith try to tame a wild horse in this film.

17. Gregory Peck is Capt. Ahab in Melville's tale of a sea captain's maniacal search for this animal.

18. Dean Jones "hires" these animals to pick olives on his farm in this Disney film.

19. This Czech film deals with a wild stallion about to be put to death and a little girl's efforts to save him.

20. Young David Ladd plays a boy who loves fish and animals, even barracudas in this film.

21. Peter Niles receives a colt as a gift, but it escapes in this Steinbeck story.

22. Van Johnson plays a song-and-dance man whose career gets a boost when he teams up with a smart dog.

23. A collie brings love and happiness to a crippled girl in this film.

24. This is the story of a dog's adventures when he

takes to the road.

25. She was the lion in *Born Free*.

26. Sal Mineo is an Indian brave who desires a wild stallion in this Disney drama.

27. Don Knotts turned into a fish and the U.S. Army's secret weapon in this comedy.

28. Celia Kaye makes friends with a wild dog who becomes her protector when she is shipwrecked in this film.

29. *Jungle Cat*, a Walt Disney documentary is about what animal?

30. A colt proves in this film that she will not be separated from the little girl she loves. Ward Bond, Donna Corcoran, and Francis Dee star.

31. Oliver Reed is assigned by the British forces to smuggle an elephant named Lacy across the Alps during WW II in this film.

32. Jimmy Stewart's co-star in this film is a six-foot invisible rabbit.

33. This Disney film stars a horse named Aspercel and Dean Jones as an advertising executive.

34. Margaret O'Brien and Walter Brennan star in this story of a girl and her horse.

35. A loveable, loyal dog sets out on a series of adventures with Brandon de Wilde and Walter Brennan in tow.

36. A baby sea monster is captured and put on display in this British Monster movie. Unfortunately for London, its mother soon comes looking for it.

37. Walt Disney produced this film about a loyal Skye terrier that cannot forget its owner.

38. Tony Randall co-stars with a large lion that provides a fair share of the laughs in this comedy.

39. He was the first X-rated animal to hit the movie screen.

40. Ray Milland battles these amphibians as they attempt to take over the world in this horror film.

41. Clint Howard is a boy who befriends this animal in *Gentle Giant*.

42. A 15-year-old Yorkshire boy trains this pet in the film *KES*.

43. Mickey Rooney and Elizabeth Taylor starred in this 1944 film of two kids who train a horse to win the Grand National. The horse and the film bear the same name.

44. Robert Lansing befriends a whale in this film.

45. Chuck Connors and Luke Halpin star in this film about the world's most delightful Dolphin. (HINT: it spawned a TV show of the same name.)

46. Bruce Davison trains an army of rats to do his bidding in this rodent-horror movie.

47. What was the name of Tarzan's faithful and comic chimpanzee?

48. In this film, a murdered dog returns to Earth in the form of Dick Powell to avenge his own murder.

49. Fred MacMurray and Anne Baxter were also in this film, but the real star of the film was a horse.

50. This late sixties film starred an otter.

51. Walt Disney filmed this comedy adventure about a nosey and heroic siamese cat.

52. Thumper the rabbit established himself as a great comic supporting character in this Disney classic. Can you name this 1942 animated film?

53. Clarence starred in this film that was later turned into the TV show, *Daktari*. What was Clarence?

54. This delightful Disney animal discovered a use for his huge ears in this animated classic. What was it called?

55. What animal was voted the most popular film performer of 1926?

56. What was the name of the dog in the *Thin Man* movies?

57. What three famous horses have their hoof prints outside Graumann's Chinese Theatre?

58. What was the baby in *Bringing Up Baby?*

59. What was Bugs Bunny's original name?

60. What was Mickey Mouse's original name?

61. Chill Wills supplied the voice for this famous talking animal.

62. What film used the most animals?

63. What famous actress owned a pet lion, named Winston?

64. A Masai Chief was so taken with what actress that

he tried to trade 150 cows and 200 goats and sheep for her during African location shooting?

65. Originally, the end of King Kong was supposed to take place where?

66. What is actor Allan Lane best known for?

67. What are the Patsy Awards?

68. What do all the Collies who played Lassie have in common?

69. What was the name of the MGM Lion?

70. What was the title of the original Lassie movie?

71. Who won the first Patsy Award?

72. Name Rin-Tin-Tin's films.*

73. He was probably the first non-human movie star in cameos for the various Max Sennett silent films.

74. Although this film claimed such stars as Roy Schneider, Robert Shaw and Richard Dreyfuss, it is probably best remembered for the performance of its mechanical white-shark villain.

75. Maurice Evans, Kim Hunter, Roddy McDowell play the apes who speak in these science-fiction films. Charlton Heston stars as the ship-wrecked astronaut.

76. In this Hitchcock thriller, creatures menace stars Tippi Hedron and Rod Taylor, not to mention most of California. What are they? (HINT: it's also the title of the film.)

77. Believe-it-or-not, the scene in It Happened One Night, where Clark Gable eats a carrot supposedly

served as inspiration for this classic, wise-cracking hare. What's his name?

78. Raymond Burr starred as the reporter who covers the rampage of this famous beast through Tokyo. Name the beast.

CHAPTER FIVE

Let's Go to the Movies

1. Jean-Paul Belmondo is a suave, dashing swindler in pre-WW II France in this film.

2. Liza Minelli plays a young woman who is afraid of the real world, but falls in love with Wendell Burton anyway.

3. Bette Davis plays twins in this film. The plot involves the murder of one sister by the other, and the take-over of her life.

4. He played the inventor of the telephone in this film.

5. Brian De Palma directed this film about a set of Siamese twins, one of whom is a murderer, and the doctor who loved them both.

6. Michael Sacks played Kurt Vonnegut's time-tripping hero in *Slaughter-House Five*.

7. Stanley Kubrick directed this epic film about a slave revolt in Rome. Kirk Douglas, Jean Simmons, and Laurence Olivier star.

8. George Brent murders deformed girls in this thriller, and mute Dorothy McGuire is next.

9. What is the name of the international organization of evil that James Bond always battles?

10. Michael Cimino directed this film with Clint Eastwood and Jeff Bridges as veterans trying to pull off a big heist.

11. Lauren Bacall and Humphrey Bogart fell in love during the filming of this movie.

12. Mario Lanza sang the song that was to become his theme, "Be My Love" in this, his second film.

13. What is the doll full of that Alan Arkin wants so desperately from Audrey Hepburn in *Wait Until Dark?*

14. Gary Grimes has a crush on the beautiful Jennifer O'Neill in this nostalgic film.

15. Goldie Hawn and Robert Atherton kidnap their own child and a state trooper before they set out on a manic chase in this film.

16. Judy Garland's big number, "Get Happy" comes from this 1950 film with Gene Kelly.

17. This Italian director's films include *The Taming of the Shrew, Brother Sun, Sister Moon,* and *Romeo and Juliet.*

18. Bruce Dern stars in this science fiction film that has him circling Saturn with man's only remaining samples of earthly plant life.

19. They play an artist and a muddled, married minister who fall in love in this film:

20. *Scream and Scream Again,* boasts a cast of three classic horror films actors. Can you name them?

21. Rod Steiger has the title role of an army officer who cannot cope with his attraction for a young private.

22. Giancarlo Giannini stars in this Lina Wertmuller tragic/comedy about a small-time hood who

accidentally became the "butcher of Naples" and ends up in a prison camp.

23. Sherlock Holmes meets Sigmond Freud could have been the sub-title for this film.

24. Tom Ewell starts thinking about neighbor Marilyn Monroe when his wife goes off on a summer vacation.

25. William Powell and Myrna Loy played them in all the "Thin Man" movies.

26. Richard Roundtree is a black detective in this film, not unlike the roll Sean Connery played as 007.

27. This is the story of submarine warfare and the rivalry of a commander, Clark Gable, and his lieutenant, Burt Lancaster.

28. The climax of this Alfred Hitchcock spy thriller takes place in the Statue of Liberty.

29. This is Ernie Kovacs' last film. It involves the robbery of a bank in Boston by ship.

30. Yukio Mishima's story of a sailor who is murdered by schoolboys stars Kris Kristofferson and Sarah Miles.

31. Jimmy Cagney stars in this picture about speakeasies, prohibition, and the heydey of gangsters.

32. Audrey Hepburn came out of a retirement of 10 years to star in this film with Sean Connery.

33. Gregory Peck doesn't have any idea Audrey Hepburn is a princess when he falls in love with her in this movie.

34. Peter O'Toole is a mad English Earl who thinks he's

Christ in this satire.

35. Tennessee Williams wrote the novel, Jose Quintero directed this story of an older woman who buys the affections of a young stud.

36. When Franco Zeffirelli filmed his verison of this Shakespeare classic, it was the thirteenth time it had been put on film.

37. Betsy Drake decides to open hers and Cary Grant's home to various problem children in this comedy-drama.

38. This film comedy traces the rise of the first all-black Madison Avenue advertising agency, called "Truth and Soul"

39. Sidney Poitier stars in this drama of a black family that escapes the ghetto by moving into a white neighborhood.

40. Jeff Bridges and Sam Waterston portray laid-back cattle rustlers in this comedy Western.

41. Bela Lugosi and Boris Karloff star in this story of a gangster and a plastic surgeon who idolizes Edgar Allen Poe.

42. Among others, the Andrews Sisters, Harry James and Joe E. Lewis are drafted in this musical about a war-time camp.

43. Charleton Heston stars in this comedy of a hard-headed, very military army man forced into taking command of a military school.

44. This Mel Brooks comedy includes a parody of musical comedies called "Springtime for Hitler" Zero Mostel and Gene Wilder star.

45. Cliff Robertson played John F. Kennedy in this WW II drama.

46. Alan Arkin has the title role in this film about a Puerto Rican widower who wants his sons to have a better life.

47. This Gershwin opera is the story of a crippled man in love with a beautiful girl. Sidney Poitier and Dorothy Dandridge star.

48. Gene Hackman as a minister tries to lead the trapped passengers of this capsized ocean liner to safety in this Irwin Allen film.

49. James Coburn is hunted by everyone from the F.B.I. to the K.G.B., to the phone company in this film. It's all because he's headshrinker for the White House.

50. The Judy Garland/Gene Kelly number, "Be A Clown" is from this film.

51. John Kerr comes to Vincent Price's Castle to investigate his sister's sudden death.

52. John Wayne and Randolph Scott are miners who fight over Marlene Dietrich in this wartime melodrama.

53. Jessica Walter is out to murder disc-jockey Clint Eastwood in this thriller.

54. Lon Chaney played the demented, disfigured killer who hides in the caverns below the open house in this classic.

55. Katharine Hepburn must choose between them in *The Philadelphia Story*.

56. Monty Wooley, as a child-hating Englishman must help a pack of them escape the Magi's spell in this film.

57. Peter Sellers is perfect as the inept Inspector Clouseau in this comedy that sparked a series of films.

58. Twin boys who play a frightening game of exchanging their identities terrorize the rest of their household in this gothic mystery.

59. Jack Lemmon and Sandy Dennis are visitors to New York who have everything happen to them that possibly could in this comedy.

60. George Segal is a frumpy book clerk who becomes involved with hooker Barbara Streisand in this film.

61. Claudette Colbert runs away from her poor husband Joel McCrea to be wooed by the rich but boring Rudy Vallee in this film.

62. Al Pacino had his first starring role in this story of junkies on Manhattan's Upper West Side.

63. They play Haley Mills' estranged parents in *The Parent Trap*.

64. He starred in *The Pawnbrokers*, as a man who'd lost faith in his fellow human beings.

65. Carol Burnett and Walter Mattheau play two ordinary, realistic people who learn to cope with tragedy in this comedy-drama.

66. Can you name Sonja Henie's first film?

67. Ava Gardner plays a Greek goddess-of-love statue come to life in this musical.

68. Jimmy Cagney, Coca-Cola, and the Cold War are all rolled together in this Billy Wilder comedy.

69. Roberto Rossellini fashioned this seminal, Italian drama about a Nazi-fighting priest in Occupied Rome.

70. Lon Chaney plays a feeble-minded giant in this screen adaptation of Steinbeck's novel.

71. Yves Montand is Barbara Streisand's psychiatrist in this musical.

72. Yul Brynner discovers that he doesn't want Kay Kendall to divorce him in this comedy.

73. Louise Fletcher won an Academy Award for her portrayal of Nurse Ratchet in this film.

74. Edward G. Robinson plays an over-age bank clerk who goes to war and comes home a hero in this film.

75. Louis Malles' film concerns the sexual initiation of a 15-year-old boy and his loving incestuous relationship with his mother.

76. This is Gary Cooper's last film. It co-starred Deborah Kerr.

77. Elaine May is an accident-prone botanist and Walter Mattheau the cad who wants to marry her in this comedy.

78. This film was the project Marilyn Monroe was involved in at the time of her death.

79. Ernest Borgnine won an Oscar for his performance as a lonely man in search of love in this film.

80. Chester Morris plays a reformed safecracker who

aids the police in the popular series that began with
this picture.

81. Jon Voight and Dustin Hoffman co-starred in this
sordid tale of 42nd St. hustlers.

82. Peter Sellers adopts Ringo Starr and sets out to
prove that anyone can be bought in this farce.

83. Ingmar Bergman filmed this performance of the
famed Mozart Opera in 1973.

84. This gap-toothed British comedian appears in
films such as *How To Murder Your Wife* and *Make
Mine Mink*.

85. David Bowie comes to Earth to discover a source of
water for his drought-struck planet in this excellent
science-fiction film.

86. Roger Moore is 007 in this, the 8th James Bond
film. Our favorite Agent must dispose of a heroin
smuggling operation.

87. Can you name the stars of Sidney Lumet's screen
adaptation of Eugene O'Neill's *Long Day's Journey
Into Night*?

88. Woody Allen parodies almost every Russian novel
in the story of a bumbler trying to stay out of the
Napoleonic wars. He falls in love with Diane Keaton.

89. This was Elvis' first movie.

90. Ali MacGraw and Ryan O'Neal fall in love despite
their differences in this film.

91. They played Ma and Pa Kettle in the popular
series.

92. Greer Garson and Walter Pidgeon starred in this film about the discoverers of radium.

93. Michael Caine and Anthony Quinn star in this tale of the occult set in the Aegean.

94. Charles Laughton swears to hunt prisoner Fredric March to the ends of the Earth in the screen adaptation of Victor Hugo's novel.

95. Sidney Poitier winds up helping Lilia Skala and some nuns build a chapel in this award-winning film.

96. Arthur Penn's film of the only survivor of the Little Big Horn, Dustin Hoffman, includes most of the history of the settling of the West.

97. Katharine Hepburn, Joan Bennett, and Frances Dee star in this screen version of Louisa May Alcott's classic.

98. Robert De Niro falls in love with Ingrid Boulting because she resembles his late wife in this screen adaptation of an F. Scott Fitzgerald novel.

99. Jack Hawkins is an ex-army officer who assembles his men one last time, for a robbery in this comedy.

100. Bob Hope and Marilyn Maxwell star in this comedy about a race-track hanger-on who owes the syndicate a fortune.

101. Dustin Hoffman plays the seminal, harrassed comic of the title in this drama.

102. Barbara Hershey, Richard Thomas, Bruce Davison and Cathy Burns play teen-agers finding out about life during a summer on Fire Island in this film.

103. Alain Resnais directed this art-house classic about an elusive, symbolic trio who cannot decide if

they've ever met.

104. Robert Benton directed this film about an aging detective and a spaced-out younger woman who solve the death of an old friend. Art Carney and Lily Tomlin star in this movie.

105. Deanna Durbin sees a murder committed and investigates on her own when no one will believe what she has witnessed.

106. Jack Nicholson and Otis Young are Navy Police sent to pick up Randy Quaid. Nicholson and Young decide to show the kid a good time before they turn him in, though.

107. Randolph Scott and Binnie Barnes star in this settler-drama about the French-Indian War.

108. Peter Bogdanovich directed this film about a small Texas town in the 50's and a young boy who grows up there.

109. Dana Wynter and Kevin McCarthy star in this tale of space creatures who invade human bodies in an attempt to take over the world.

110. Paul Muni portrays Mexico's greatest hero, lawyer and statesman in this film.

111. Deborah Kerr tutors the children of the King of Siam in this musical. BONUS QUESTION: Yul Brynner played the King in this musical; who played the opinionated monarch in the non-musical, 1948, version?

112. He directed the thriller, *Lady from Shanghai*, with Rita Hayworth. He also stars in it.

113. Robert Morse and Michelle Lee star in this

"instruction" musical on how to quickly climb the corporate ladder.

114. Paul Newman has no regard for anything, which leads him into direct conflict with his iron-willed father, Melvyn Douglas in this movie.

115. Red Skelton as a zany presser falls for Eleanor Powell in this comedy.

116. Susan Hayward portrays a real-life crook, Barbara Graham, who was sent to the gas chamber. Ms. Hayward won an Oscar for her performance.

117. Ida Lupino and Humphrey Bogart star in this drama of a killer and the ensuing manhunt.

118. Fred Astaire and Bing Crosby dance and sing their way through Irving Berlin's songs in this musical about a hotel.

119. Tony Curtis stars as the world's greatest magician and escape artist in this film.

120. Widower Cary Grant hires Sophia Loren as a housekeeper and babysitter in this sophisticated comedy.

121. Elaine May directed this comedy about a newly-married couple whose marriage disintegrates on their honeymoon thanks to Cybill Shepherd. Charles Grodin and Jeannie Berlin are the couple.

122. Shirley Temple has the title role in this classic Swiss tale of a mountain girl who cannot survive in the city.

123. Gene Kelly directed this musical, with Barbara Streisand as a marriage broker, and Walter Mattheau as the buyer.

124. Gary Cooper is on his own in this western about a sheriff unable to get any help when a gang of outlaws come to kill him.

125. James Garner and Richard Attenborough star in this movie about allied P.O.W.'s during WW II. One of the highlights is Steve McQueen's motorcycle-escape scene.

126. Robert Redford stars as an aerial stunt-pilot in the 1920's who regrets missing WW I.

127. Burt Lancaster and Kirk Douglas join forces as Wyatt Earp and Doc Holliday to rid Tombstone of the notorious Clanton gang.

128. Gregory Peck, David Niven, and Anthony Quinn head the all-star cast in this war thriller. The plot revolves around the allied destruction of the German's most heavily-fortified Aegean defense posts.

129. Elvis and Shelly Fabrares fall in love in Fort Lauderdale during her college vacation.

130. June Allison and Jimmy Stewart star in this story of the originator of the big band sound.

131. Charlie Chaplin ends up eating his shoe in this comedy-classic set in the Klondike.

132. Marlene Dietrich is a gypsy who hides British spy Ray Milland in this comedy/adventure film.

133. Ali MacGraw and Richard Benjamin both debuted in this Philip Roth story of a Jewish dropout in love with a country club girl.

134. Norma Shearer had the title role in this costume drama about the court of Louis XVI. Robert Morley

was the Sun King, and Tyrone Power co-starred as Ms. Shearer's romantic interest.

135. Lynn Redgrave had her first starring role as a shy, ugly English girl who "lives" through the exciting lives of others.

136. Tom Ewell, Jane Mansfield, and Edmond O'Brien star in this story of washed-up promotor, a gangster, and a girl who becomes a star in spite of everything. Little Richard and Eddie Cocoran make guest appearances.

137. Clifton Webb and Edmund Gwenn are bored angels who save a mortal couple's marriage in this film.

138. Gary Cooper and Ingrid Bergman star in Hemingway's story of people involved in the Spanish Civil War.

139. Anne Francis and Leslie Nielson fall in love in this story of a scientist with something to hide far from the Earth.

140. Dominique Sanda and Helmut Berger star in Vittoria de Sica's film of the disintegration of a Jewish family in Mussolini's Italy.

141. Keir Dullea interferes in the relationship of Sandy Dennis and Anne Heywood in this screen adaptation of D.H. Lawrence's story.

142. This film examines life among the weird members of a circus sideshow, with the main parts played by performers who are actually deformed. This film has become a cult classic.

143. Lotte Lenya and Robert Shaw would both like to see Sean Connery (as James Bond) dead, in this film.

144. Lucille Ball co-stars with Eddie Albert in this comedy of the mis-haps and adventures of a traveling saleswoman.

145. Sean Connery and Joanne Woodward star as a loud mouthed, radical poet and his flippant, funny wife in this zany comedy.

146. Spike Jones and Buddy Hackett star in this wacko, slapstick comedy about a turn-of-the-century fire-department and their adventures.

147. Jimmy Stewart, Peter Finch and Richard Attenborough survive a plane crash only to be faced with the perils of the desert of this film.

148. John Wayne is the squadron leader in this WW II drama of flying aces battling the Japanese.

149. Rosalind Russell hires Fred MacMurray as her secretary and (of course) falls in love with him in this comedy.

150. Ronald Coleman and Edna May Oliver star in this faithful telling of Dicken's tale of the French Revolution.

151. Topol and Molly Picon star in this musical about Ukranian Jews and the happenings in their village.

152. Ethel Merman belted out "Heat Wave" in this 1938 film.

153. This all-singing, all-dancing extravaganza was written by Stephen Vincent Benet. The plot involves a family of brothers' search for wives.

154. Although they were only supporting characters in *Flying Down to Rio*, they created a dance style when they did "the Carioca."

155. Fred Astaire danced on the walls and ceiling of his room in a scene from this musical.

156. Anthony Quinn and Alan Bates star in this film about a passionate Greek who teaches an up-tight Englishman how to live.

157. Dean Jagger won an Oscar for his performance in this WW II flying drama. It also starred Gregory Peck, Hugh Marlow and Gary Merrill.

158. Charles Boyer tried to rid himself of Ingrid Bergman in this film by convincing her that she was mad.

159. Jane Wyman was critically acclaimed in this film about a deaf-mute.

160. Ethel Waters and Lena Horne were Cab Calloway's co-stars in this 1943 black musical showcase.

161. Bing Crosby won his first Oscar for his portrayal of a priest in this famous film.

162. Name Dick Powell's films with Ruby Keeler.

163. Brando's musical, with Frank Sinatra and Jean Simmons.

164. This forgotten, silent masterpiece by Abel Gance was recently resurrected by Francis Ford Coppola.

165. His portrayal of the waif in this Charlie Chaplin film made him a star.

166. Irene Dunne plays the wife recently rescued from a deserted island and Cary Grant the husband about to re-wed in this Garson Kanin comedy.

167. Name the three film classics John Ford won Academy Awards for directing.

168. This was Garbo's first Hollywood film.

169. This cult-film director's films include *In A Lonely Place*, *Johnny Guitar*, and *Rebel Without a Cause*.

170. James Stewart temporarily laid-up in his apartment, witnesses a murder in this Hitchcock nail-biter.

171. Can you name the films Marlene Dietrich made for Josef von Sternberg in Hollywood?

172. Erick von Stroheim considered this silent film his masterpiece, even though the original 42 reels were reduced to ten.

173. Doris Day made her debut in this 1948 musical.

174. She was billed as "the yodeling commedienne" in films like *Chatterbox*.

175. Lizabeth Scott "helps" Humphrey Bogart solve the murder of his veteran buddy in this film.

176. James Coburn plays a flip, charming con-man in this film about a bank robbery.

177. Marlon Brando played Napoleon to Merle Oberon's Josephine in this film.

178. Four stars have played the soft-spoken, law-upholding Western hero Destry in the movies. Can you name them?

179. His parting line to her. "I hope they don't hang you, precious, by that sweet neck." devastated movie audiences.

180. Randolph Scott played one of his finest roles as the hero of H. Rider Haggard's story of an immortal white goddess.

181. Humphrey Bogart married Lauren Bacall just days after his divorce from this actress. The press called them the "Battling Bogarts."

182. These two big box-office directors of the seventies team up for this action/adventure yarn, *Raiders of the Lost Ark*.

183. In *Letter to Three Wives* they played the three women.

184. *Lust For Life* starred Kirk Douglas as this troubled, genius painter.

185. John Huston starred Humphrey Bogart in six of his films. Can you name them?

186. Shirley Temple is left with Adolphe Menjou as security on an I.O.U. in this 1934 film comedy.

187. Tyrone Power and Gene Tierney star in this screen adaptation of W. Somerset Maugham's novel.

188. Name the stars cast as Gary Cooper's brother in the 1939 film, *Beau Geste*.

189. Many critics consider this W.C. Fields film to be his funniest and most consistent comedy.

190. In *The African Queen*, Humphrey Bogart is attached to only one thing, and it isn't Katharine Hepburn.

191. This comedy about a Russian submarine that runs aground off the shore of Nantucket stars Carl Reiner and Alan Arkin.

192. William Holden made his debut in the starring role of a prize fighter in this 1939 film.

193. This 1953 John Ford western starring John Wayne

was actually filmed in 3-D, although it was never released in that form.

194. Grace Kelly made only 11 movies in her brief career; three of them were for Alfred Hitchcock. Can you name them?

195. Laurence Olivier, Noel Coward, Ralph Richardson, Alfred Hitchcock, and Charlie Chaplin all have one thing in common.

196. This was Bruce Lee's first Hollywood Kung-Fu film. In it, he plays a marital arts expert enlisted to round up drug smugglers.

197. Robert Mitchum, John Wayne, Richard Burton and Red Buttons head the all-star cast in this epic WW II film. Among other distinctions, this movie about the Normany invasion was the most expensive black and white film ever produced.

198. Walt Disney claimed he modeled this animated character after Marilyn Monroe.

199. This thriller by Fritz Lang starred Peter Lorre, and was Germany's first talking picture.

200. A phrase in Latin appears underneath the MGM Lion, Leo, at the beginning of all this studio's films. What is it?

201. Shirley MacLaine, a dancer, had a non-dancing role in this ballet film. Her co-star, Anne Bancroft, a non-dancer played an aging ballerina.

202. Actress Mercedes McCambridge provided the voice of Linda Blair when she becomes possessed in this horror film.

203. Bruce Cabot rescues Fay Wray from the clutches of this enraged, giant movie ape.

204. Paul Muni plays a dedicated general practitioner in Brooklyn in this, his last film.

205. Jane Wyman, Patty Duke, and John Mills, all have one thing in common; they have all won Oscars for portraying mutes. Can you name the films they won for?

206. Clark Gable, Charles Laughton, and Franchot Tone were all nominated for best actor for their work in this film.

207. James Dean was set to play the lead in this film about the life of boxer Rocky Graziano, when he died in a car crash. Paul Newman took over the role.

208. Clark Gable and Carole Lombard appeared together in only one film; can you name it?

209. Tennessee Williams wrote the part of Blanche DuBois for Tallulah Bankhead. Vivian Leigh ended up playing her in this film.

210. Orson Welles, Joseph Cotton and Agnes Moorhead all made their screen acting debuts in this 1941 film. Can you name it?

211. Jane Fonda, Gig Young, Susannah York and Red Buttons all turned in exceptional performances in this film about the Depression's marathon dance contests.

212. Name Errol Flynn's first film and the one that made him a star.

213. It is common knowledge that Humphrey Bogart and Ingrid Bergman starred in *Casablanca*, but can you name the two players originally slated for those famous roles?

214. In his film, he was called "the little Tramp" and he was also the first actor to grace the cover of Time

Magazine.

215. Robert Duvall and Donald Pleasance star in this vision of the future as completely dehumanized, politically oppressing,   made by a young director who went on to make (among others) *Star Wars*.

216. Although there may be over ten versions of this film classic around, Richard Lester's is certainly among the best. Can you name this Alexander Dumas classic which stars Michael York, Oliver Reed, and Faye Dunaway, among others?

217. Joanne Woodward won an Oscar for her portrayal of a woman with three distinct personalities.

218. Marlon Brando and Lee Marvin's acting in this seminal motorcycle film contribute to its tension and suspense.

219. Christopher Jones and Hal Holbrook starred in this imaginary takeover of the U.S. Government by a rock-singing President. Everyone over 30 is shipped to a camp in this late-60's drama.

220. James Mason played the evil Capt. Nemo in Walt Disney's adaptation of Jules Verne's classic about a cosmic-powered submarine.

221. Hitchcock only directed one film comedy, with Carole Lombard and Gene Raymond.

222. Hitchcock directed, and Joan Fontaine and Cary Grant starred in, this 1941 thriller. Fontaine begins to suspect that Grant is going to murder her for her money.

223. Fredric March and Veronica Lake star in this film about a gubernatorial candidate and a 300-year-old witch that falls in love with him.

224. Ralph Byrd played this famous cartoon hero in this film.

225. Greta Garbo and Clark Gable appeared together in only one film.

226. Claude Raines starred as Jack Griffin in this science-fiction thriller, although we never got to see his face.

227. Name the first James Bond movie.

228. In 1939, all but one of the major Academy Awards went to this motion picture.

229. This is the only film veteran director George Cukor ever won an Oscar for.

230. James Cagney made only three Westerns. Can you name them?

231. His reply to Walter Huston's muttered oath was "If you want to call me that, smile."

232. Gary Cooper and Marlene Dietrich fell in love in this story of the Foreign Legion.

233. Dolores Del Rio was Joel McCrea's romantic interest in this island adventure film.

234. Alan Young and Dinah Shore star in this classic tale of a widow and a con-man.

235. Tyrone Power is forced to decide which of the 20-odd passengers of a lifeboat must die so that the rest can live.

236. Loretta Young plays a schoolteacher who accidentally kills an over-attentive student in this film.

237. Henry Fonda and Lee J. Cobb head up an all-star

cast as a jury that must decide whether a young boy knifed his father to death.

238. Frank Zappa created this cult classic about the Mothers of Invention and groupies they encounter on the road.

239. Francois Truffaut starred in and directed this story of an abandoned child raised by wolves.

240. The Beatles star in this animated tale of Pepperland and its invasion by Blue Meanies.

241. Gene Wilder and Marty Feldman star in this zany comedy about a famous detective's inept younger brother.

242. Bogart is pitted against Nazi-spies in this thriller. Phil Silvers and Peter Lorre co-star.

243. Patty McCormick plays the evilest of little girls in her role as a six-year old murderess in this film.

244. Cyd Charrisse and Fred Astaire dance their way through this film about the trials of a Broadway show.

245. Ava Gardner takes over the Jean Harlow role in this 1953 remake of *Red Dust*. Both films starred Clark Gable.

246. Burt Lancaster, Dean Martin, and Jacqueline Bisset star in this first-in-a-series of airborne disaster movies.

247. Arlo Guthrie stars in this film version of his hit song.

248. An African tribe allows Cornell Wilde a fighting chance for survival in the jungle.

249. Gregory Peck and Lee Remick discover they have

given birth to the Anti-Christ in this macabre tale of horror.

250. Ingmar Bergman's psychological study of withdrawal and role reversal stars Liv Ullman and Bibi Anderson.

251. Elinor of Aquitaine as portrayed by Katharine Hepburn and Henry the II, acted by Peter O'Toole, are the main points of interest in this film.

252. Edward G. Robinson's performance as a "menace to society" lifts this film above all other gangster movies.

253. Alain Resnais created this art-film classic about the love between a French actress and a Japanese architect after WW II.

254. Alan Arkin portrays a deaf-mute in this tale of human perseverance in the face of cruelty.

255. Julie Andrews and Max von Sydow star in this epic of settlers in the 50th State.

256. Eva Marie Saint and Don Murray star in this story of a junkie, and the people who try to help him.

257. Bette Davis is a fast-living woman who discovers she is dying in this tear-jerker.

258. An Academy Award was given to Julie Christie for her portrayal of a socially ambitious model in swinging London. Dick Bogarde and Laurence Harvey also star.

259. A wealthy bachelor, played by Fred Astaire, supports a young girl with the stipulation that she never learn his identity. Leslie Caron co-stars in this delightful musical.

260. Jose Ferrer plays this classic hero with a large nose in love with the beautiful Roxanne.

261. An amiable, slow-moving cowboy played by Gary Cooper is nearly gunned down when mistaken for a killer in this comedy-western.

262. Fellini takes a look at Italian village life in the 1930's in this fine film. His touch is much lighter in this examination of life in a seaside village under Fascism, than in most of his current work.

263. A twelve-year-old boy joins up with con-man Steve McQueen in this film adaptation of Faulkner's novel.

264. Charles Laughton is cast as (perhaps) the greatest Dutch painter in this film biography.

265. Zero Mostel turns into the creature of the title in this 1974 film adaptation of an Ionesco play.

266. The devil is the father of Mia Farrow's child in Roman Polanski's film about modern witchcraft.

267. Clark Gable and Loretta Young star in this film adaptation of Jack London's Klondike tales.

268. Richard Harris, Franco Nero, and Vanessa Redgrave star in this musical about King Arthur's Court.

269. Art Garfunkel and Jack Nicholson star in Mike Nichol's study of sexual hang-ups and adventures.

270. This sprawling film is a parody of James Bond films. David Niven and Peter Sellers are just two of the stars in this epic.

271. Lee Marvin plays a duo role in this black comedy western. Jane Fonda has the title role.

272. Jack Benny and Ann Sheridan are city-slickers who move to a farmhouse in the sticks in this comedy.

273. Sam Peckenpah directed this stylishly-violent bank-heist film with Steve McQueen and Ali McGraw.

274. Rex Harrison plays the ghost of a sea captain who befriends Gene Tierney in this film that gave rise to a TV show of the same name.

275. Rock Hudson and James Dean are both in love with Elizabeth Taylor in this sprawling film about oil empires in the West.

276. Claudette Colbert starred in this film about a woman who becomes famous by rejecting a royal marriage.

277. Architect Stanford White's murder is the focus of this film starring Ray Milland and Farley Granger.

278. Sean Connery and Honor Blackman, star in this third film in the James Bond series. It involves the intricate robbery of Fort Knox.

279. This epic film swept up 8 Academy Awards in 1939, including Best Actress for its star, Vivien Leigh. This Civil War film also stars Clark Gable, Leslie Howard and Olivia de Haviland.

280. Jack Carson holds down the title role in this slapstick comedy about an ice-cream man who becomes involved with gangsters.

281. Peter O'Toole and Petula Clark star in this musical remake of the 1938 film with Robert Donat and Greer Garson. O'Toole portrays a mawkish professor who marries a beautiful young actress while on Holiday.

282. Jean Gabin and Erick von Stroheim star in

Renoir's classic tale of the First World War.

283. Robert Redford and Mia Farrow star in F. Scott Fitzgerald's story of wealth and the wealthy in the 1920's.

284. Stanley Kubricks cast Ryan O'Neal as a socially ambitious 18th Century rogue in this epic.

285. Frankie Avalon and Annette Funicello began a series of beach-party films with this movie.

286. Jerry Lewis stars as a nervous, bungling bellboy at a resort hotel in this comedy.

287. *The Guardsman* is the only film this most famous of theatre couples ever made. It is the story of an Austrian actor who goes to incredible lengths to test his wife's fidelity.

288. Sidney Poitier falls in love with Spencer Tracy and Katharine Hepburn's daughter in this film about the tensions of inter-racial love.

289. Victor Mature has his job cut out for him as the head of a circus, with Red Buttons and Rhonda Fleming as performers.

290. Glenn Ford goes after the gangsters who killed his wife, with the help of Gloria Grahame. Lee Marvin is excellent as a vicious, menacing hood in this drama.

291. Walter Pidgeon and Gilles Payant star in this Disney drama. The boy loves an Irish Setter that belongs to Walter Pidgeon, which is how the tale begins.

292. Burt Lancaster becomes an expert on birds while serving a murder rap.

293. This 1975 Louis Malle film casts Kathryn Grayson

in a bizarre, often surrealistic Alice-In-Wonderland World. There is war going on between men and women and she escapes into a secluded house of talking rats, unicorns, midgets and Joe D'Allesandro.

294. Glenn Ford is a new teacher in a tough school in this film. His pupils include a tough, problematic Sidney Poitier and a knife-carrying Vic Morrow.

295. Mel Brooks created this zany comedy that stars Cleavon Little as a black sheriff in a town that boasts Madelaine Kahn as a saloon singer and Harvey Corman as a man who hangs horses, among other things.

296. Shelley Winters is Ma Barker in this blood-filled gangster film.

297. Alan Ladd finds himself under suspicion for his faithless wife's murder in this crime drama. William Bendix is great as his best friend who is injured in the war and who may have done it.

298. Judy Holiday won an Oscar for portrayal of a scatter-brained blonde in this film. William Holden and Broderick Crawford are her co-stars.

299. Cliff Gorman and Laurence Luckinbill star in the 1970 film of Mart Crowley's play. The plot involves a group of homosexuals who throw a birthday party and the ensuing pathos.

300. Father Flannigan's home for boys is the subject of this film. Spencer Tracy plays the Father and Mickey Rooney stars as a boy who is nothing but trouble.

301. John Garfield and Patricia Neal star in this crime/love story based on a Hemingway tale.

302. Boris Karloff is the classic monster and Elsa Lancaster the mate that is "made" for him in this

horror film.

303. Jimmy Stewart is a scout and Jeff Chandler is Cochise in this Western drama.

304. Bette Davis, Karen Black and Oliver Reed star in this off-beat horror tale about a house that slowly takes over the personality of a woman living in it.

305. Ethel Merman is "the hostess with the mostess" in this Irving Berlin musical about the Washington social scene.

306. Great character actor Guy Kibbee is Shirley Temple's guardian in this film about a lighthouse keeper and a waif.

307. Piper Laurie is Sissey Spacek's Bible-spouting, crazed mother in this tale of psychokinetic powers.

308. Elizabeth Taylor and Paul Newman are an embattled husband and wife in this southern drama by Tennessee Williams. Burl Ives is impressive as Newman's father, "Big Daddy."

309. War in all its absurdities is presented in this adaptation of Joseph Heller's book. Alan Arkin stars as Yossarian, a very sane man desperately trying to be classified mad.

310. Audrey Hepburn and Cary Grant are the stars of this sophisticated comedy/mystery. The plot involves the theft by Miss Hepburn's late husband of a quarter-of-a-million in gold. His co-conspirators want it back and they are sure she knows where it is.

311. Clifton Webb rules the roost of a very large family in this comedy/drama. Jeanne Crain and Myrna Loy co-star.

312. Loretta Lynn comes to the Big Screen in the form

of Sissy Spacek in this film about the singer's life.

313. John Hurt and Anthony Hopkins star in this story of the horribly deformed John Merrick.

314. Jerry Lewis returns to the screen in this typical comedy about an unemployed clown and the jobs he attempts to work in.

315. Michael Serrault and Ugo Tognazzi are everyone's favorite gay couple in this comedy. This blatantly funny French film focuses on the marriage of one of the lovers' son to a high political-officer's daughter.

316. Robert Redford directed this film about a family touched by tragedy. Mary Tyler Moore, Timothy Hutton and Donald Sutherland star.

317. Dame May Whitty simply disappears from the train car she is riding in. Margaret Lockwood and Michael Redgrave are determined to solve the mystery in this Hitchcock film.

318. Alec Guinness manages to steal a million pounds from the Bank of England in this comedy.

319 A love/hate relationship between punks Robert De Niro and Harvey Kietel is the focus of this Martin Scorsese film.

320. Dan Dailey is a small-time dreamer and Celeste Holmes is his incredibly understanding wife in this light comedy.

321. Jean-Louis Barrault is a mime who falls for a beautiful woman who breaks his heart in this lengthy, French cult-film.

322. James Caan is a sailor who falls for Marsha Mason in this film. The catch is that Mason has an 11-year-old

child by a black sailor.

323. This is the Marx Brothers first film. The plot revolves around the Florida land boom and a hotel manager's efforts to get in on it.

324. An entire town tries to quit smoking in this comedy starring Dick Van Dyke.

325. A battle of wits between Bogart and Sidney Greenstreet is the main excitement of this mystery. Bogie murders his wife, and Greenstreet is determined to break his perfect alibi.

326. Bing Crosby stars in this musical version of Mark Twain's story of a time traveler who ends up in Camelot.

327. As a strong-willed prisoner on a chain gang, Paul Newman gives one of his best performances. George Kennedy won an Academy Award for his performance as a sadistic leader of the gang.

328. Rita Hayworth works her way up from the chorus line to become a top model in this musical. Gene Kelly co-stars.

329. Glenn Ford and Donald O'Connor star in this comedy of service men who are forced to turn their Geisha House paradise into an orphanage to keep their command happy.

330. Humphrey Bogart spends the first quarter of the film in bandages. The plot involves a man who must change his face after he escapes from prison.

331. W.C. Fields, Lionell Barrymore and Maureen O'Sullivan star in George Cukor's adaptation of the Classic Dickens tale.

332. Ethel Barrymore is a newspaper publisher kept

from giving up by her editor, Humphrey Bogart.

333. Fredric March is Willie Loman, a rapidly fading salesman in this drama of family relationships.

334. James Fenimore Cooper's tale of the settling of American colonies stars Lex Barker and Forrest Tucker.

335. Tony Curtis and Sidney Poitier are chain-gang convicts who escape in this drama. Their escape is made all the more difficult by their racial hatreds and the fact that they are chained together.

336. Jon Voight and Burt Reynolds get more than they bargained for in their canoe trip down a Georgia river.

337. James Mason is Rommel, and Richard Burton commands the Australian Forces in the WW II film.

338. A beautiful jewel thief seduces an innocent young man to help her smuggle her prize home. Marlene Deitrich is the thief, and Gary Cooper the young man in this drama.

339. Katharine Hepburn is in danger of losing her job when Spencer Tracy automates her section of a Broadcasting company in this comedy.

340. Billy Wilder took home three Oscars for this 1960 film, best picture, best director and best screenplay.

341. Bing Crosby was nominated for two separate Oscars for playing the same character in two different films. Can you name them?

342. Peter O'Toole is the only other character to share Bing Crosby's distinction. Can you name the films he was nominated for?

343. Woody Allen stayed in New York to play the-

clarient rather than fly to Hollywood to accept the three Oscars he won for this film.

344. Buster Keaton suggested that Fatty Arbuckle change his name after the scandal of his manslaughter trial. Arbuckle did eventually direct a few features under the name "William Goodrich," but can you name the one that Keaton suggested?

345. William Bendix portrayed this baseball great in the 1948 film biography.

346. James Caan played Billy Rose and Barbara Streisand once again played Fanny Brice in this film.

347. Steve McQueen had his first starring role in this 1958 film about a gelatinous substance that starts to envelope the world.

348. William Boyd was the famous white-haired cowboy in this series of popular westerns.

349. Walter Brennan is the only actor to win three Academy Awards for his supporting roles. Can you name the movies.

350. Although Alec Guiness played the part of Colonel Nicholson in this war film, it was originally offered to another famous British actor.

351. Bugs Bunny, as we know him today, made his debut in this 1940 cartoon.

352. Gary Cooper, Errol Flynn, Warner Baxter and Ronald Coleman were all considered for the male lead in this epic film of the Civil War. Clark Gable finally landed the role. What was the film and who did he play.

353. Marilyn Chambers was originally an Ivory Soap baby, long before her emergence as a porno queen in

this film.

354. Jeff Chandler played Cochise in three movies. Can you name them?

355. Charlie Chaplin had a comic strip modeled after him in 1916. Can you name it?

356. Charlie Chaplin made his final film appearance in a cameo bit in this movie.

357. Charlie Chan, the great Chinese movie detective has never been portrayed on-screen by a Chinese man. Can you name the seven stars who've played him in the movies?

358. James Cagney portrayed George M. Cohan in these two movies.

359. He is the only movie actor to receive the Congressional Medal of Honor.

360. Shirley Booth made her movie debut in this drama of a marriage on the rocks. Burt Lancaster is her alcoholic husband.

361. Cartoonist Milton Caniff claimed he modeled her features on those of Joan Crawford.

362. She has the distinction among actresses of being the only female president of the Academy of Motion Picture Arts and Sciences.

363. Joan Fontaine is sister to this other famous actress.

364. Sally Kellerman plays Hot Lips Houlihan in this black comedy about medical units during the Korean War.

365. This is the only film, a Western, that Marlon

Brando directed and starred in.

366. Woody Allen starred along with Zero Mostel and Hershel Bernardi in this movie about black-listed actors and writers in the heyday of McCarthyism.

367. MGM auctioned off a prop of Judy Garland's in 1970 at the famous sale. What was it and how much did it fetch?

368. Garson Kanin and Ruth Gordon have been nominated for Academy Awards for two screenplays that (both) starred Hepburn and Tracey. Can you name them?

369. Cary Grant never said this phrase in any of his films, but it helped to make him famous.

370. Gene Hackman won an Oscar for his depiction of Popeye Doyle in this police/smuggling drama.

371. Marilyn Monroe and Jean Harlow both co-starred with Clark Gable in their last films. Can you name them?

372. Charles Laughton, Robert Shaw and Richard Burton have all portrayed King Henry VIII in films. Name them.

373. Edward G. Robinson and Barbara Stanwyck are perfect as an insurance agent and a scheming wife who plot to kill her husband and collect in this Billy Wilder movie.

374. This box office giant employed the talents of Charlton Heston, Ava Gardner, Lorne Greene and Sensurround to tell its story.

375. James Dean starred in this film of adolescent rebellion against a tyrannical father.

376. Sean Connery returned to the role of James Bond in this international thriller about diamond smugglers.

377. An excellent cast, among them Marie Dressler, John and Lionel Barrymore, Billie Burke, and Harlow combine to make this comedy a perennial favorite of revival houses.

378. Can you name the full title of the Stanley Kubrick black comedy about the unintentionable nuclear bombing of Russia? Its stars include Peter Sellers, George C. Scott, and Slim Pickins.

379. Dick Powell and Ellen Drew played the prize-winners in this 1940 comedy, *Christmas in July*, but who directed?

380. This drama fictionalized the sensational Leopold-Loeb murder case.

381. This Francis Ford Coppola film was ignored at the box office, and Gene Hackman's performance is brilliant.

382. Ten detective/crime thrillers, in a series were produced in the forties and all starred Warner Baxter. What was the first one called?

383. United Artists advertised this film with the slogan "a lion in your lap." Robert Stack and Nigel Bruce star in this 1952 Natural Vision 3-D movie.

384. Jackie Cooper played the child who had faith in Wallace Beery as a (has been) boxer in this 1931 tear-jerker.

385. Lillian Hellman wrote it, William Wyler directed, and Audrey Hepburn and Shirley MacLaine starred in this story of the power of a lie.

386. Fred Astaire danced "Putting on the Ritz" in this Paramount musical that also starred Bing Crosby.

387. Ken Russell cast Twiggy as the star of this over-inflated, camped up musical from the early seventies. Name the film.

388. Otto Preminger cast Laurence Olivier, Carol Lynley, and Noel Coward in this movie of mystery and deceit.

389. Can you name the first black horror film?

390. Arthur Lake and Penny Singleton immortalized the cartoon-strip family the Bumsteads in this series of comedies from the 30's and 40's.

391. Michelangelo Antonioni's vision of swinging London and the slim line between reality and illusion made this movie a huge success in the 60's.

392. Ronald Reagan co-starred with a chimpanzee in these two 50's comedies. Can you name them?

393. Ramon Navarro starred in the silent version, with Charlton Heston holding down the title role in this re-make.

394. Raymond Chandler wrote it, Howard Hawks directed, and Bogart and Bacall star in this complicated, smokey mystery.

395. Katharine Hepburn debuted in this George Cukor film about a strong-willed daughter who meets her father for the first time, after a long stay in a mental institution. John Barrymore played the father.

396. Terrence Malick created this cult film of senseless murder. It starred Martin Sheen and Sissy Spacek.

397. Peter Cook and Dudley Moore wreak havoc with

the Faustian legend in this camp comedy. Can you name it?

398. Nicholas Ray has the distinction of making classic cult movies. Can you name his four films?

399. *Of Human Bondage* has gone before the cameras three times: once in 1934, once in 1946, and once in 1964. Can you name the mis-matched lovers in each version?

400. Name the four actors and directors who formed United Artists in 1919.

401. What was the first silent movie to win an Academy Award?

402. John Wayne met Montgomery Clift in this Western.

403. John Wayne, Gary Cooper, and Lee Marvin all hold one piece of movie trivia in common. Do you know what it is?

404. Alan Ladd played the tight-lipped title role, with Van Heflin as the homesteader he helps in this Western. Can you name the movie?

405. Bruce Dern killed John Wayne in this Western.

406. John Ford directed it, John Wayne became a star because of it, and the opening sequence is considered the model for all great Westerns.

407. Robert Altman cast Warren Beatty and Julie Christie in his off-beat story of western expansion and personal decay.

408. Jack Nicholson shared the screen for the first time with Marlon Brando in this western.

409. Tom Laughlin made movie history and a fortune as the title role in this low-budget, modern day western.

410. This John Wayne movie has become a certified cult-film in America. Jeffrey Hunter and Natalie Wood join him in this tale of obsession.

411. Claudette Colbert and Henry Fonda fall for each other in this settlers/Indians conflict movie.

412. Astaire and Kelly danced together only once, in this film.

413. Name Liberace's musicals.

414. Clifton Webb and Dana Andrews engaged in a game of wits in this mystery.

415. This film made stars of Warren Beatty, Faye Dunaway, Gene Hackman and Estelle Parsons.

416. What was the first movie filmed in Hollywood?

417. What was the first 3-D movie?

418. Name the only film all three Barrymores (John, Ethel and Lionel) appeared in together?

419. What was the first CinemaScope movie?

420. Lillian Gish starred in this 1912 silent movie by D.W. Griffith. In it, he examined the slums of lower-east side Manhattan and made what was to become the first gangster film.

421. Name Mary Pickford's two biggest screen successes.

422. How many films did Fred Astaire and Ginger Rogers make together?

423. Can you name the film Ginger Rogers won an Academy Award for? (HINT: It was a non-singing, non-dancing film which *did not* co-star Astaire.)

424. Carole Lombard and John Barrymore starred in this screwball comedy of a producer who must convince an adamant star to appear in his next production.

425. Dustin Hoffman starred in this 1971 mystery with one of the longest film titles ever.

426. Lindsay Anderson cast Malcolm McDowell in this powerful film about the senseless disciplines of the English Boarding School.

427. Maggie Smith's tour-de-force performance as the head of an exclusive girls' school made this film stand out.

428. This is probably Alfred Hitchcock's best known film, starring Anthony Perkins and Janet Leigh. The extreme terror evoked by the shower scene shows you exactly what's wrong with today's show-it-all violence.

429. Woody Allen won an Oscar for this film of a love affair that failed. Diane Keaton proved the perfect co-star and foil for his humor.

430. Garbo, Joan Crawford, the Barrymore's, and Wallace Beery starred in this film of love and heartbreak in a magnificent hotel.

431. Bette Midler played a Janis Joplin-like star on the way down in this movie.

432. This film of disillusionment and alienation made Jack Nicholson a star.

433. *The Deer Hunter* netted a slew of Oscars, but this

director's second film has given him nothing but trouble. It stars Kris Kristoferson and Isabelle Hupert.

434. Peter O'Toole re-surfaces in this film of deceit, trickery and movie life.

435. Robert Duvall stars in a critically-acclaimed role as a gung-ho marine who runs his family as if it were the corp.

436. In 1923, Harold Lloyd made what is probably his best known film, if only for the famous scene where he clings to the side of a very high building. Can you name it?

437. Hollywood, in the twenties, appointed him as czar of the screen stars morals, and he quickly inserted "morality clauses" in most star's studio contracts.

438. This film was advertised with the simple slogan, "Garbo Talks."

439. Among his films were *The Phantom of the Opera*, *West of Zanzibar*, *The Hunchback of Notre Dame*, and his only talkie, *The Unholy Three*. He was called "the man of a thousand faces."

440. Can you name the film in which Mae West said "Goodness has nothing to do with it, honey?"

441. Marlene Dietrich boosted her sagging career and Jimmy Stewart turned this old Tom Mix western into an excellent film. Can you name it?

442. Clifton Webb introduced one of his best known characters Mr. Belvedere, in this film.

443. Can you name James Dean's three starring films?

444. Name the two films Gary Cooper won his two

Oscars for.

445. They starred in the first version of an aging star on the way down and a new one on the way up who became involved.

446. Hedy Lamarr and Charles Boyer starred in this film that made "come with me to the Casbah" a household catch-phrase.

447. Jane Russell starred in this western, with Howard Hughes directing and producing. Although it wasn't released for three years after completion, Miss Russell became a star overnight because of the publicity stills of her in the hay.

448. Name Ken Russel's three film biographies of composers.

449. Originally John Travolta was to have played opposite Lauren Hutton in this story of a big-time male hustler. He was replaced by Richard Gere. What was the film?

450. Marlon Brando holds the record for the most money ever paid an actor up front for a film. Name the film and the amount.

451. This classic horror story by Robert Lewis Stevenson has been filmed for the movies twenty-four times.

452. Katharine Hepburn co-starred with Spencer Tracy in what was to be his last film.

453. Together in 1938 they made the first of an immensely popular series of films. Judy Garland and Mickey Rooney played the leads, with Lewis Stone as Mickey's almost perfect father, the Judge.

454. Name the first all-talking film in color.

455. This film was the first feature length cartoon ever presented.

456. This was the first film for which a soundtrack album was also produced.

457. Merle Oberon's car crack-up halted production of this Roman Epic, directed by Josef von Sternberg and also starring Charles Laughton. Production was never resumed, but the remaining bits point to this film's unfinished greatness.

458. Can you name the first film released in CinemaScope?

459. Filmed as one of Irving Thalberg's "prestige" films, this film starred Paul Muni and Luise Rainer as Pearl S. Buck's hard-working Chinese peasants. It took four years to film, and went through two producers and directors.

460. This top-grossing film of 1937 was a precursor to Irwin Allen's disaster films. It starred Dorothy Lamour, Jon Hall, Mary Astor and the screen's largest tropical storm.

461. Ronald Coleman and Douglas Fairbanks, Jr. were enemies in this swahbuckling film that co-starred Madeleine Carroll and Raymond Massey.

462. How many films did William Powell and Myrna Loy star in together?

463. Director Max Reinhardt cast a strickly Hollywood crew in this 1935 version of a Shakespeare comedy.

CHAPTER ONE
ANSWERS

1. Paula Prentiss
2. Eileen Brennan
3. Patricia Neal and Jack Albertson
4. Mercedes McCambridge
5. Martin Balsam
6. Rossano Brazzi
7. Greer Garson
8. Nancy Olson
9. Orson Welles
10. Angela Lansbury
11. Arnold Schwarzenegger
12. Robert Shaw
13. Alec Guinness
14. James Earl Jones
15. R2D2 and C3PO
16. Peter Cushing
17. Ethel Barrymore
18. Claire Bloom
19. Eartha Kitt, Ella Fitzgerald
20. Sig Ruman
21. Jennifer Salt
22. Diane Keaton
23. *Small Change*
24. *Soylint Green*
25. Jodie Foster
26. Martin Scorsese
27. Conrad Veidt
28. Charlton Heston
29. Janice Rule
30. Adolfo Celi
31. Eleanor Parker
32. Walter Brennan
33. Judy Geeson
34. "Who" drummer, Keith Moon
35. Billie Burke
36. *Joseph Cotton, Marlene Dietrich and Mercedes McCambridge*

37. Paul Scofield
38. Melvyn Douglas
39. Jonathan Winters
40. Anthony Quinn
41. Efrem Zimbalist, Jr.
42. Ricky Nelson
43. Richard Benjamin
44. Ed Begley
45. James MacArthur, Tommy Kirk and Kevin Corcoran
46. Charlotte Rampling
47. Rita Moreno
48. John Barrymore
49. Ruth Gordon
50. Red Buttons
51. Godfrey Cambridge
52. Estelle Parsons
53. Earl Holliman
54. Slim Pickins
55. Jerry Lacy
56. Anthony Perkins
57. Lilli Palmer
58. Jane Wyman
59. Jack Albertson
60. Rita Hayworth
61. John Houseman
62. Madelaine Kahn
63. Diane Varsi starred as Allison, and Hope Lange played Selena
64. Alec Guinness
65. Shirley Jones
66. William Dix
67. Beatrice Straight
68. Claude Rains
69. Rod Steiger
70. Ron Moody
71. Diana Rigg
72. Brad Dourif
73. Ernie Kovacs
74. Laurence Olivier
75. Eli Wallach

76. Vanessa Redgrave
77. Jean Arthur
78. Roy Scheider
79. Judy Garland and Margaret O'Brien
80. Pola Negri
81. Jack Lemmon
82. Robert Duvall
83. Elke Sommers
84. Jack Carson
85. Beatrice Arthur
86. Buck Henry
87. Lee Marvin
88. Mark Rydell
89. Angela Lansbury
90. Liberace
91. Donald Sutherland
92. Jack Nicholson
93. Peter Ustinov
94. Maureen Stapleton
95. (1) Kay Kendall
    (2) Mitzi Gaynor
    (3) Taina Elg
96. C. Aubrey Smith
97. Adolphe Menjou
98. Jean-Pierre Leaud
99. Jeanne Moreau
100. Jack Nicholson
101. Vincent Price
102. Marcel Bozzuffi
103. Robert Shaw
104. Ellen Burstyn
105. (1) Cloris Leachman
     (2) Ben Johnson
106. Kay Medford
107. Ben Vereen
108. *The Greatest Story Every Told*
109. Agnes Moorehead
110 Thomas Mitchell
111. Claire Trevor

112. Walter Mattheau
113. Binnie Barnes
114. Paul Henreid
115. Victor Mature
116. Thelma Ritter
117. Jason Robards, Jr.
118. Virginia Weilder
119. Sam Jaffe
120. Frank Shannon
121. Laura Hope Crews
122. Dwight Frye
123. Walter Brennan
124. Gale Sondergaard
125. Lee Tracy
126. Jerome Cowan
127. Jack Carson
128. Donna Reed
129. Brandon de Wilde
130. Lee Marvin
131. Nigel Bruce
132. Joel Grey
133. Jim Backus
134. Alan Arkin
135 Gary Merrill
136. Kay Thompson
137. Eric Blore
138. Hoagy Carmichael
139. Hattie McDaniel, for her portrayal of Mammy in
Gone With The Wind.
140. Five
    (1) Professor Marvel
    (2) The Wizard
    (3) The Gatesman
    (4) The Driver of the Horse of a Different Color
    (5) The Wizard's Guard.
141. Adolphe Menjou
142. Burgess Meredith
143. Frank Lawton
144. Howard Duff in The Late Show

145. Zachary Scott
146. Julie Andrews
147. Noah Beery
148. Ina Claire
149 Brian Donlevy
150. Jean Rogers
151. Erich Von Stroheim
152. George Segal and Sandy Dennis
153. Eli Wallach
154. Shelley Winters
155. Franklin Pangborn
156. Donald Crisp
157. Walter Burke
158. Claude Rains as Captain Renault
159. Anthony Quinn
160. Edmund Gwen
161. Thelma Ritter
162. Alfred Hyde-White
163. Fidel Castro
164. Chief John Big Tree
165. Lewis Stone
166. Zazu Pitts
167. Frankie Thomas
168. Butterfly McQueen
169. Larry Simms
170. Monty Wooly
171. Elsa Lanchester
172. Arthur O'Connell
173. Everett Sloan
174. Walter Connolly
175. Alan Hale
176. Edward Everett Horton
177. Steven Geray
178. Conrad Veidt
179. Helen Westley
180. Alice Brady
181. Elizabeth Patterson
182. Charles Buttersworth
183. Una O'Connor

184. George Tobias
185. Victor Bruno
186. Eugene Pallette
187. Frank McHugh
188. Elsa Lanchester
189. Florence Bates
190. George Saunders
191. Peter Lorre
192. Peggy Hopkins Joyce
193. C. Aubrey Smith
194. Cecilia Parker
195. Dooley Wilson
196. Virginia Christine
197. John Carradine
198. Ellen Corby
199. He has made over 191 films.
200. Norma Varden
201. Mary Wickes
202. George Zucco
203. Elisha Cook
204. George "Gabby" Hayes

CHAPTER TWO
ANSWERS

1. Natalie Wood
2. Liza Minelli
3. Bette Davis
4. Susan George
5. Margot Kidder
6. Barbara Feldon
7. Candice Bergen
8. Cicely Tyson
9. Shirley MacLaine
10. Joanne Woodward
11. Gene Tierney
12. Shelly Duvall and Sissy Spacek
13. Julie Christie
14. Debbie Reynolds
15. Marilyn Monroe
16. Carole Lombard
17. Gena Rowlands
18. Betty Hutton
19. June Allyson
20. Deborah Kerr
21. Dorothy McGuire
22. Shirley MacLaine
23. Judy Holiday
24. Miriam Hopkins
25. Madeleine Carroll
26. Barbara Streisand
27. Susannah York
28. Helen Hayes
29. Alice Faye
30. Jill Clayburgh
31. Talia Shire
32. Elizabeth Taylor
33. Ruby Keeler
34. Jane Withers
35. Mary Astor

36. Sophie Tucker
37. Eleanor Powell
38. Louise Brooks
39. Josette Day
40. Giulietta Masina
41. Patty Duke and Anne Bancroft
42. Lee Remick
43. Ursula Andress
44. Greer Garson
45. Evelyn Venable
46. The woman was Gloria Grahame; the reply was "I said I liked it. I didn't say I wanted to kiss it."
47. Ava Gardner
48. Ann Sheridan
49. Judy Holiday
50. Angela Lansbury
51. Patty Duke
52. Elizabeth Taylor for *Cleopatra*
53. Deanna Durbin
54. Barbara Streisand in *Up The Sandbox*
55. Joan Crawford
56. Marlene Dietrich in *Angel*
57. Loretta Young
58. Raquel Welch
59. Catharine Deneuve in *Belle de Jour*
60. Gwen Verdon
61. Sandy Dennis
62. Margaret Rutherford
63. Liza Minelli
64. Doris Day
65. Rita Hayworth
66. (1) *Dark Passage*
    (2) *Key Largo*
    (3) *To Have and Have Not*
67. Jane Russell and Marilyn Monroe
68. Gloria Grahame
69. Ida Lupino
70. Veronica Lake
71. Ingrid Bergman

72. Julie Andrews and the film was *Mary Poppins*
73. (1) Funny Face
    (2) My Fair Lady
74. Alexis Smith
75. Jean Seberg
76. Shirley MacLaine
77. Alice Faye
78. Lena Horne
79. Ethel Merman
80. Esther Williams
81. (1) *A Place in the Sun*
    (2) *Raintree County*
    (3) *Suddenly Last Summer*
82. (1) *Country Girl*
    (2) *High Society*
83. (1) Claudette Colbert
    (2) Vivien Leigh
84. Jean Simmons
85. Margorie Main
86. Simone Signoret
87. Dorothy Lamour
88. Joan Fontaine
89. Olivia de Havilland
90. Katharine Hepburn.
91. Claudette Colbert
92. Reportedly, she said, "No, dear...the "T" is silent, like in Harlot."
93. Barbara Streisand
94. Judy Garland
95. Audrey Hepburn
96. Eleven
97. Shirley Temple
98. *There's One Born Every Minute*
99. *The Women*
100. Vivian Leigh, Lauren Bacall and Rosalind Russell
101. Marilyn Monroe
102. Nine
103. Tatum O'Neal, age 10, for *Paper Moon*
104. Sonja Henie

CHAPTER THREE
ANSWERS

1. Marlon Brando
2. Warren Beatty
3. Vittorio De Sica in *The Monte Carlo Story*
4. Cary Grant
5. Donald Sutherland
6. Montgomery Clift
7. Marlon Brando
8. Gerard Depardieu and Patrick Dewaere
9. George Peppard
10. Donald Houston
11. Bruce Dern
12. Gene Hackman
13. Gene Hackman and Al Pacino
14. Erland Josephson
15. Richard Attenborough
16. Montgomery Clift
17. Robert Young
18. Rock Hudson
19. Pat O'Brien
20. Dean Stockwell
21. David Niven
22. Frank Sinatra, Dean Martin, and Sammy Davis, Jr.
23. Dirk Bogarde
24. Raymond Massey
25. Steve McQueen in the title role and Robert Preston as his father.
26. Douglas Fairbanks, Jr.
27. Michael Crawford and Oliver Reed
28. George Raft
29. Peter Boyle
30. Ted Neely
31. Robby Benson
32. Robert Redford
33. Roy Scheider
34. Michael York

35. Edward Albert
36. Alan Bates
37. Elliott Gould and Robert Blake
38. Jan-Michael Vincent
39. Edward G. Robinson
40. Donald Barthelmess
41. Alec Guinness
42. Van Johnson
43. Bud Cort
44. George Peppard
45. Vittorio De Sica
46. David Carradine
47. Robert Culp and Elliott Gould
48. George Segal
49. Tyrone Power
50. George Arliss
51. Melvyn Douglas
52. James MacArthur
53. Jackie Cooper
54. Monty Wooly
55. Cameron Mitchell
56. Vincent Price
57. James Coburn
58. Beau Bridges
59. Charles Boyer
60. George Segal and James Fox
61. Alan Bates
62. Charles Chaplin
63. John Travolta
64. Charleton Heston as British General Charles
    Gordon and Laurence Olivier as the Arab, Mahdi.
65. Audie Murphy
66. Peter Lawford
67. Paul Scofield
68. Terence Stamp
69. Rod Steiger
70. Jon Voight
71. Michael Redgrave
72. Sir Ralph Richardson

73. Paul Robeson
74. Maximilian Schell
75. Tab Hunter
76. Billy Dee Williams
77. John Wayne
78. Alec Guinness and Peter Sellers
79. Jack Palance
80. Gregory Peck
81. Christopher Plummer
82. Sidney Poitier
83. Steve McQueen
84. Karl Malden
85. Walter Mattheau
86. Yves Montand
87. Burt Lancaster
88. Stan Laurel and Oliver Hardy
89. Peter Lorre
90. Joel McCrea
91. Curt Jurgens
92. Boris Karloff
93. Buster Keaton
94. Charleton Heston
95. Dennis Hopper
96. Rock Hudson
97. Toshiro Mifune
98. Rex Harrison
99. Laurence Harvey
100. Sessue Hayakawa
101. Van Heflin
102. Cary Grant
103. Alec Guinness
104. Richard Dreyfus
105. Richard Harris
106. Gene Kelly
107. Donald O'Connor
108. Mick Jagger
109. John Barrymore
110. Alan Bates
111. Warren Beatty

112. Wallace Beery
113. Jean-Paul Belmondo
114. Humphrey Bogart
115. Joe E. Brown
116 Yul Brynner
117. Richard Burton
118. Michael Caine
119. John Casavettes
120. Montgomery Clift
121. Ronald Coleman
122. Sean Connery
123. Jackie Coogan
124. Gary Cooper
125. Noel Coward
126. Broderick Crawford
127. Helmut Berger
128. Kirk Douglas
129. Clint Eastwood
130. Douglas Fairbanks, Senior
131. Peter Finch
132. Henry Fonda
133. Glenn Ford
134. Clark Gable
135. John Garfield
136. John Gilbert
137. Elliott Gould
138. Alan Ladd
139. *Giant*
140. Boris Karloff
141. Kirk Douglas
142. Peter Fonda and Dennis Hopper
143. Lee Tracy
144. (1) Leo Gorcey
     (2) Huntz Hall
     (3) Bobby Jordan
     (4) Gabriel Dell
145. George Burns, at age 80, for *The Sunshine Boys*
146. Frank Sinatra
147. Richard Burton, with 7 nominations

148. Ward Bond
149. John Travolta
150. *Laura*
151. Lon Chaney, Jr.
152. Vincent Price and Edward G. Robinson
153. Frank Sinatra
154. Peter Lorre
155. Conrad Veidt
156. James Cagney
157. Richard Conte
158. Farley Granger and Robert Walker
159. Buddy Ebsen
160. Maurice Chevalier
161. Danny Kaye
162. Spencer Tracy
163. Robert Wagner
164. Orson Welles and Joseph Cotton
165. Gregory Peck
166. Montgomery Clift
167. *Raintree County*
168. William Holden
169. Donald O'Connor
170. George C. Scott

CHAPTER FOUR
ANSWERS

1. Race Horses, in *My Brother Talks to Horses*
2. *My Pal Wolf*
3. *Old Yeller*
4. *The Painted Hills*
5. *Clash of the Titans*
6. A German Shepherd dog, in the Disney film, *Smoke*
7. *Smoky*
8. *Snowfire*
9. *The Story of Seabiscuit*
10. *The Black Stallion*
11. *Tiko and the Shark*
12. *Tony*
13. *Two Little Bears*
14. *Maya*
15. *Mighty Joe Young*
16. *Misty*
17. The Whale, *Moby Dick*
18. Chimpanzees in *Monkeys Go Home*
19. *The Proud Stallion*
20. *Raymie*
21. *The Red Pony*
22. *Kelly and Me*
23. *Lad: a dog*
24. *The Littlest Hobo*
25. *Elsa*
26. *A Horse Named Comanche*
27. *The Incredible Mr. Limpat*
28. *Island of the Blue Dolphins*
29. Jaguars in the Amazon Rain Forest
30. *Gypsy Colt*
31. *Hannibal Brooks*
32. *Harvey*
33. *The Horse in the Gray Flannel Suit*
34. *Glory*
35. *Goodbye, My Lady*

36. *Gorgo*
37. *Greyfriar's Bobby*
38. *Fluffy*
39. *Fritz the Cat*
40. *Frogs*
41. An Alaskan Grizzly Bear
42. A Kestrel Hawk
43. *National Velvet*
44. *Namu, The Killer Whale*
45. *Flipper*
46. *Willard*
47. Cheetah
48. *You Never Can Tell*
49. *Smokey*
50. *Ring of Bright Water*
51. *That Darn Cat*
52. *Bambi*
53. A cross-eyed lion
54. *Dumbo*
55. Rin Tin Tin
56. Asta
57. (1) Tony, Tom Mix's horse
    (2) Trigger, Roy Roger's horse
    (3) Champion, Gene Autry's horse
58. A leopard
59. Happy Rabbit
60. Mortimer Mouse
61. Francis the Talking Mule
62. *Around the World in Eighty Days*
    3,800 sheep
    2,448 buffalo
    950 donkeys
    800 horses
    512 monkeys
    17 bulls
    15 elephants
    6 skunks
    4 ostriches

63. Tallulah Bankhead
64. Carroll Baker
65. Yankee Stadium
66. The voice of the talking horse, Mr. Ed
67. Picture Animal Top Star of the Year
68. They were all males
69. Leo
70. *Lassie Come Home*
71. Francis, The Talking Mule
72. (1) *The Night Cry*
    (2) *The Lone Defender*
    (3) *The Lightning Warrior*
    (4) *The Wolf Dog*

*Rin-Tin-Tin, Jr. made two follow-up films, (1)*The Law of the Wild*, and (2) *The Adventures of Rex and Rinty*

73. Ben, a loving mutt
74. *Jaws*
75. *Planet of the Apes*
76. Birds, in *The Birds*
77. Bugs Bunny
78. Godzilla

CHAPTER FIVE
ANSWERS

1. *Stavisky*
2. *The Sterile Cuckoo*
3. *Stolen Life*
4. Don Ameche in the *Story of Alexander Graham Bell*
5. *Sisters*
6. Billy Pilgrim
7. *Spartacus*
8. *Spiral Staircase*
9. Spectre
10. *Thunderbolt and Lightfoot*
11. *To Have and Have Not*
12. *The Toast of New Orleans*
13. Heroin
14. *Summer of '42*
15. *The Sugarland Express*
16. *Summer Stock*
17. Franco Zeffirelli
18. *Silent Running*
19. Elizabeth Taylor and Richard Burton in *The Sandpipers*
20. Vincent Price, Peter Cushing and Christopher Lee
21. *The Sergeant*
22. *Seven Beauties*
23. *The Seven-Percent Solution*
24. *The Seven Year Itch*
25. Nick and Nora Charles
26. *Shaft*
27. *Run Silent, Run Deep*
28. *Saboteur*
29. *Sail A Crooked Ship*
30. *The Sailor That Fell From Grace With The Sea*
31. *The Roaring Twenties*
32. *Robin and Marion*
33. Roman Holiday
34. *The Ruling Class*
35. *The Roman Spring of Mrs. Stone*, with Viven Leigh and Warren Beatty

36. *Romeo and Juliet*, with Leonard Whiting and Olivia Hussey as the lovers
37. *Room For One More*
38. *Putney Swope*
39. *A Raisin in the Sun*
40. *Rancho Deluxe*
41. *The Raven*
42. *Private Buckaroo*
43. *The Private War of Major Benson*
44. *The Producers*
45. *PT 109*
46. *Popi*
47. *Porgy and Bess*
48. *The Poseidon Adventure*
49. *The President's Analyst*
50. *The Pirate*
51. *The Pit and the Pendulum*
52. *Pittsburgh*
53. *Play Misty for Me*
54. *Phantom of the Opera*
55. Cary Grant and Jimmy Stewart
56. *The Pied Piper*
57. *The Pink Panther*
58. *The Other*
59. *The Out-Of Towners*
60. *The Owl and the Pussycat*
61. *The Palm Beach Story*
62. *Panic in Needle Park*
63. Maureen O'Hara and Brian Keith
64. Rod Steiger
65. *Pete 'n' Tillie*
66. *One in a Million*, with Don Ameche and the Ritz Brothers
67. *One Touch of Venus*
68. *One, Two, Three*
69. *Open City*
70. *Of Mice and Men*
71. *On A Clear Day You Can See Forever*
72. *Once More With Feeling*
73. *One Flew Over The Cuckoo's Nest*
74. *Mr. Winkle Goes to War*

75. *Murmur of the Heart*
76. *The Naked Edge*
77. *A New Leaf*
78. *Something's Got To Give*, it was never finished
79. *Marty*
80. *Meet Boston Blackie*
81. *Midnight Cowboy*
82. *The Magic Christian*
83. *The Magic Flute*
84. Terry Thomas
85. *The Man Who Fell To Earth*
86. *Live and Let Die*
87. (1) Katharine Hepburn
    (2) Ralph Richardson
    (3) Jason Robards, Jr.
    (4) Dean Stockwell
88. *Love and Death*
89. *Love Me Tender*
90. *Love Story*
91. Marjorie Main and Percy Kilbride
92. *Madame Curie*
93. *The Magus*
94. *Les Miserables*
95. *Lilies of the Field*
96. *Little Big Man*
97. *Little Women*
98. *The Last Tycoon*
99. *The League of Gentlemen*
100. *The Lemon Drop Kid*
101. *Lenny*
102. *Last Summer*
103. *Last Year at Marienbad*
104. *The Late Show*
105. *Lady on a Train*
106. *The Last Detail*
107. *The Last of the Mohicans*
108. *The Last Picture Show*
109. *Invasion of the Body Snatchers*
110. *Juarez*
111. *The King and I*
     Bonus Question: Rex Harrison

     (2) Joel McCrea
     (3) Audie Murphy
     (4) James Stewart
179. Humphrey Bogart to Mary Astor at the end of *The Maltese Falcon*
180. *She*
181. Virginia Mayo
182. Stephen Speilberg (as director) and George Lukas (as producer)
183. (1) Ann Southern
     (2) Linda Darnell
     (3) Jeanne Crain
184. Vincent van Gogh
185. (1) *Beat the Devil*
     (2) *Across the Pacific*
     (3) *Key Largo*
     (4) *The African Queen*
     (5) *The Maltese Falcon*
     (6) *The Treasure of the Sierra Madre*
186. *Little Miss Marker*
187. *The Razor's Edge*
188. Robert Preston and Ray Milland
189. *The Bank Dick*
190. Gin
191. *The Russians Are Coming, The Russians Are Coming*
192. *Golden Boy*
193. *Hondo*
194. (1) *Dial M for Murder*
     (2) *Rear Window*
     (3) *To Catch A Thief*
195. They have all been knighted
196. *Enter the Dragon*
197. *The Longest Day.* It cost over $17 million to make this epic.
198. Tinker Belle in *Peter Pan*
199. M
200. "Ars Gratia Artis", which translates to "art for art's sake".
201. *The Turning Point*
202. *The Exorcist*

203. *King Kong*
204. *The Last Angry Man*
205. (1) Jane Wyman won for her role in *Johnny Belinda*
    (2) Patty Duke won for her role in *The Miracle Worker*
    (3) John Mills won for his role in *Ryan's Daughter*
206. *Mutiny on the Bounty*
207. *Somebody Up There Likes Me*
208. *No Man of Her Own*
209. *A Streetcar Named Desire*
210 *Citizen Kane*
211. *They Shoot Horses, Don't They?*
212. *Captain Blood*
213. Ronald Reagan and Ann Sheridan
214. Charlie Chaplin
215. *THX 1138*, 1971 by George Lukas
216. *The Three Musketeers*
217. *The Three Faces of Eve*
218. *The Wild Ones*
219 *Wild in the Streets*
220 *20,000 Leagues Under the Sea*
221 *Mr. and Mrs. Smith*
222. *Suspicion*
223. *I Married A Witch*
224. Dick Tracy in *Dick Tracy's G-Men*
225. *Susan Lenox: Her Fall and Rise*
226. *The Invisible Man*
227. *Dr. No*
228. *Gone With The Wind*
229. *My Fair Lady*
230. (1) *The Oklahoma Kid*
    (2) *Run For Cover*
    (3) *Tribute to a Bad Man*
231. Gary Cooper in *The Virginian*
232. *Morocco*
233. *Bird of Paradise*
234. *Aaron Slick from Punkin Crick*
235. *Abandon Ship*
236. *The Accused*
237. *Twelve Angry Men*